40 BELOW

EDMONTON'S WINTER ANTHOLOGY

EDITED BY JASON LEE NORMAN

WUFNIKS PRESS

WUFNIKS PRESS
EDMONTON, ALBERTA
CANADA

WWW.40BELOWPROJECT.CA
WWW.WUFNIKS.COM

40 Below: Edmonton's Winter Anthology
©2013 by Wufniks Press and the authors.

ISBN 978-0-9880196-4-5

Cover design and layout by Jason Blower
www.jasonblower.com

Interior layout by Julie Lundy
www.goodmorningjulie.com

Additional editing by Shereen Zink, Lamya Asiff

Printed and bound in Canada by Friesens Corporation
www.friesens.com

This anthology was made possible by the generous support of the Edmonton Arts Council

FOR GEO

TABLE OF CONTENTS

DARE

JANNIE EDWARDS

Who was it who said
Happiness writes white?

Bring on the blizzards!

Harness the sled dogs!

A CHRISTMAS BABY

VERNON R. WISHART

It was the winter of 1958. While the weather outside was frightful, it began to look like Christmas Day would be special. The doctor informed us that our second child might be born on December 25th. Christmas came and went, however, and the anticipated arrival did not take place.

When the baby was almost two weeks overdue, the doctor, hoping to trigger labour, prescribed for Jo, my wife, two ounces of castor oil. When that didn't produce the desired results, Jo took matters into her own hands. She drank two ounces more! Surprise! The contractions began at five minute intervals, and at two in the morning. After a quick consultation with the doctor over the phone, we bundled ourselves and our one-year-old son Jim into the car and headed to the University Hospital.

It was one of those January nights in Edmonton when the temperature was 35 below and the streets were treacherously icy. Those wintry conditions, however, soon paled in importance. Each groan from my wife, following a spasm of pain, was translated directly to my foot on the gas pedal. As the time between each contraction decreased, the speed of the car and my anxiety increased.

Approaching 112th Street from 87th Avenue, the street light was flashing red. For a split second I entertained the thought of stopping. Another groan from Jo decided the matter. I sped through the red light. As I made the turn, I caught a glimpse of what I hoped I wouldn't see—a police car poised, waiting and watching. Anxiously, I looked in my rearview mirror. The long arm of the law was in hot pursuit. A flashing light signalled me to pull over. I skidded to a stop. Clutching our son in my arms, I jumped out. A policeman, whose size was accentuated by his buffalo robe coat and a beaver skin hat, got out of the cruiser and approached with ominous intent. Frantically, I blurted, "My wife is going to have a baby at any moment!"

Dark eyes beneath the fur-skinned hat scanned the occupant of the car. I sucked in the cold air and waited for the verdict. Another sudden contraction and a sharp cry of pain from Jo swung the decision in our favour. "Follow me," he shouted. Dutifully, I followed the cruiser as it sped us to Emergency.

As I held our son in one arm and helped Jo out of the car with the other, she suddenly went rigid and cried through clenched teeth, "I don't dare move!" By now the officer had grasped the gravity of the situation. He dashed to the emergency room door and shouted, "There's a lady out here who's going to drop something!" In a matter of seconds a stretcher appeared. While Jo was being lifted gingerly onto the gurney, a nurse made a hurried diagnosis and determined what it was she was going to drop.

Expectant mother and anxious father were whisked up the elevator to the delivery room. Seventeen minutes later a baby girl was born.

I was beginning to breathe easier when I suddenly realized that I had lost track of her brother. In a state of panic, I rushed to the waiting room. There, nestled in the right arm of the police officer, was our son.

Beth was born in the wee morning hours of January 7th, 1959. She arrived on the day that those who follow the Julian calendar celebrate Christmas.

On a frosty winter's morning, while the temperature was dropping out of sight, we had an Edmonton winter's gift, a Christmas baby—an unorthodox birth on an Orthodox Christmas.

WALL OF SNOW

ALICE MAJOR

Wall of snow west of Edmonton
says the weather report.
Wall of Snow. Wall of Doom.

We're just not ready for the midway terror,
the bungee jump into boots and parkas,
the headlong hurtle into drifts.
Not yet, not yet. The cotoneaster bush
is still rosy with leaves. Clear lemon on elms.
There's fine rain in the air. It could be Vancouver here.
We wish it was.

We don't want the death-defying thrill. It will kill us
this time. We will be walled up alive
like some poor pile of bones in a castle keep.
We will return to haunt the downtown pedway system
with cold hands, cold breath, our heads tucked
underneath our arms, fur-rimmed faces staring ghastly
at passers-by.

The wind proclaims approaching storm.
It shrills down Jasper Avenue, a wailing wall.
We mourn, we mourn. We weep,
we petition for rescue—knowing it will come
six months too late.

A GIFT, TENDERED

ALICE MAJOR

Outside, houses behind high, banked snow —
like heads choked by white collars. Inside,
his black cheek against the taxi windshield,
the meter ticking to his stories of Nairobi.

Chatter of markets spun with swirled cloth
and dust and light motes. The voices of his parents.
At last, I asked him, "Why come here? Why
come so many thousand miles from home?"

Feeling it must be hard to face the weather
and the work he's over-educated for. Thinking
of the prejudices, concealed like fists
punched down in pockets.

To answer, he spoke of hope
for his children, chances they would have
even if he drove cab all his life.
And then he said,

> You just don't know
> how peaceful
> things are here
> > And later, he said again
> > There is peace here.

> Peace.

A word that became, with his saying it, something
tangible and blessed. Something spacious —
a field to open your arms in, under a fragile,
robin's-egg sky.

And something small, ordinary as dust sifting
in sunlight. Not a thing within my
gift, not a box to be held out by a white hand.
But something we might hold together,
                             hold in trust
for this place, which holds us.

OPTICAL MOLASSES

ALICE MAJOR

Winter's light approaches us,
blue-shifted, gelatinous—
a Doppler contraption that will herd us
into slower and slower motion,
a condensate of cold weather.
Under its needled ether
we contract, huddle down together—
atoms nearly frozen

into a syrup where the individual
is rendered indistinguishable.
But this down-parka-puffy-oneness
is fragile, fractures too easily.
Molecules collapse,
our pulled taffy snaps.

"Optical molasses" is a technique of cooling atoms down close to absolute zero until they become a condensate—all the atoms are exactly the same. However this state is very fragile and hard to maintain.

MY FIRST WILD WINTER

AMIR BAHARUN

Like tourists eager to see Africa's wildlife in my village, since my arrival to Edmonton, I was eager to see the Canadian wild winter. Sometime in late October, I turned on The Weather Network. I saw a snow storm warning from Environment Canada blinking ominously at the bottom of the TV screen. I glanced out the window at the swaying naked trees, waiting to welcome my first wild winter with snowflakes, something I had never seen before.

"Don't worry, Abdul, it is on its way," said Ali, my brother-in-law, with a smile. Since my arrival he had rarely smiled at me, let alone called me by name. Sometimes I saw bitterness in his face, as he came home from work looking down and cursing his lot. I thought I might have stolen his private moments with Shamsu, his wife. But she told me he was unhappy with his minimum wage job.

When he had come to our African village with three neighbouring elders and a prominent livestock dealer to ask my father for Shamsu's hand in marriage, everyone talked about his wealth and education. The next morning, he came with three well-fed milking cows and a Canadian hundred dollar bill as a dowry to marry my sister. My mother and the neighbourhood women danced and ululated in joy. For my father, it was the best business transaction he had ever made and rushed to close the deal as soon as he could. Earlier that month he had traded my half-sister for only a pair of bearded goats. At the time, I was a sixth-grade student and Ali told me he was a chartered accountant and I believed him. Years later I discovered that he was not a chartered accountant and he still had trouble with English.

I joined my sister in the kitchen when I heard her calling my name. I thought she was asking for help, but she just mentioned my name while talking on her cell phone.

After turning off her cell phone and tasting the steaming slow-cooked beef tail stew with a wooden spoon, she said, "Despite living for several years in Canada, I always feel depressed and tired during the winter season. As you gradually accustom yourself to the Canadian weather, you'll stop getting excited for snow and winter."

Snow started to come down thick and fast and Ali called me to the window to see it for myself. I put down the lettuce I was washing, and joined him in the living room. I stood holding the window sill staring in awe at the snowflakes. I smiled at the sight, as if I were getting the smile back in kind. A wise old man once told me that even death smiles at a dying person, if a dying person smiles at death. Since then, I always smiled at everyone who met my eyes as if I were an idiot.

At the dinner table, when my sister and her husband started eating, I sat on my chair thinking of the snow. The snow I had known back home was a hail storm that destroyed plants and hurt the people, and the elders would call it a sign of God's rage. Ali kept looking at me and smiling between bites. I ate in silence, while Shamsu and Ali talked about their day at work and the gossip revolving around our Ethiopian community.

After dinner, I decided to step outside in the storm to feel the snow and walk under and through it. As a child my mother used to tell me playing under the rain would help me grow tall like a weed. So, every winter, whether there was a storm or not, I ran wild under the rain and soaked my clothes. I knew the snowstorm would not help me grow up any taller, but I imagined it would be fun to walk under it.

"Who would go out in this stormy cold weather?" Ali said, holding a toothpick between his fingers. "If you would, it freezes your butt off."

"Early snow will not last long," Shamsu said to her husband, as she prepared to do the dishes. "Let him enjoy it."

"What do you know about Canadian winter? What were you before I made you my wife? You were just an ordinary African village girl. Now you live in a strange place you would have hardly ever imagined."

Shamsu did not answer, as if she was worn out by his constant quarrelling, but I was very hurt by his comment. When I looked at her she seemed like she was on the brink of tears. When I turned my head to look at him, he shot me a hostile look.

My sister was about twenty years younger than her husband and understood my desire to feel the snow. I stood up to get ready for a walk, but he asked me to wait until the storm's lull. I refused to let the snowstorm pass and insisted, like an impatient child, to walk under the gentle snowflakes. My sister helped me dress up as though I were a small child. I put on Ali's winter coat, ski pants, knitted mittens, hat with earflaps, thick socks, warm ankle-length boots, and finally a wool scarf to wrap around my neck. I suddenly became as fat as our village baker's son.

"I hope you don't get sick," Ali said, as he lit a cigarette. "Believe me, it is not fun to walk in this kind of weather."

I left the apartment without uttering a word like a man on a mission. My mission was to discover something that I had never experienced before: white and fluffy snowflakes. When I opened our fourth floor apartment unit door, there was a strong suffocating smell of something burning in a nearby kitchen, and I heard a baby scream, followed by the voice of a female tenderly trying to comfort it. I tried to descend the staircase carefully while covering my nose with my mitten. On the third floor, the smell transformed into that of sizzling onions cooking on a stove. The second floor had my favourite tangy and familiar scent of Ethiopian spice and I heard a loud noise accompanied by the sound of several people laughing in unison. The main floor had the sour smell of curry. Every apartment unit sent out a unique smell of its own speciality through its door.

My sister and her husband were living in a low-rise building, where most of the tenants were newly-arrived landed immigrants and refugees from around the world. Ali called the building a transit point, but he considered himself luggage lost in transit. The caretaker of the building whom I interviewed for my English as Second Language (ESL) class project told me that the tenants came from four continents and twelve countries. He also told me that the whole neighbourhood once was a decent place to live, but later became inner-city, a center of new immigrants and the society's underprivileged.

The main entrance was busy with tenants and visitors. They talked loudly with exotic languages like mine, but I barely understood what they said with the exception of a few funnily-pronounced English words. I exchanged greetings with the only neighbours I knew, the security guard and his janitor wife. They were eating sandwiches and exhaled out clouds that smelled of raw garlic, which neutralised for a few seconds the smell I got from within the building. Others in the lobby looked at me as if I were something of a curiosity.

Outside, everywhere was white just as I had expected it to be, and nothing escaped the falling snowflakes. On the sidewalk, I marched onwards, the matted snowflakes compressing together underneath my feet. My heart pounded like I was on my first date. When I looked up, the sky was dark without the moon or the stars as if they had migrated to the south like snowbirds. The snow was still falling gently and landing on me. The first snowflake that landed on me was unique; if it were an insect, I would have put it in the insect bottle trap.

The falling snow was like a kind of snow I had seen in the movies, and I could hardly believe that I was walking on real snowflakes. I waddled like a hockey player or a penguin with my winter jacket and pants. Not only the road but all parked cars, buildings and trees were covered with thick snowflakes and to feel them, I took my mitten off and touched them, picking up a handful from a nearby car. The falling snowflakes reminded me of locust swarms from the horn of Africa. Although I had heard stories of Canadian wild weather through my sister before I came, I still did not expect the thing I was seeing. I felt like I was dreaming and it was the most beautiful scene I had ever seen. I enjoyed walking in the street, despite gusts of wind and the falling thick snow. The gusting wind was hard, but not hard enough to dissuade me from walking. The snow-covered cars moved as usual, but the drivers drove cautiously. People walked with their heads bent down, as if they were bowing to the snow out of fear or respect, watching their footsteps. I thought the people would stop moving and stay in their homes during the storm, but it was life as usual. No one was hibernating like the neighbouring mountain grizzly bears. I walked three blocks, crossing roads carefully, then turned left on 107th Avenue and kept going. Sometimes, when no one was walking around me, I stuck my tongue out to taste the falling snowflakes. I stopped sticking my tongue out after a female motorist showed me her middle finger.

I was 25, but I felt like I was 8 as I walked under the snow. I would have liked to run and jump; sing and dance under the falling snow, but my winter dress restrained me. As the snow piled high on the sidewalks, my feet started to sink into snowflakes, I saw two young women walking in the middle of the road. One of the women asked me how long I had been in Canada. I told her only for five weeks. She threw a snowball at me, as if it was to welcome me.

My face felt burning cold and almost frozen from the gust of wind. I was exposed to the heat and hot weather, but not to the cold that burns human flesh. My mother used to say, "A human face and a young person should never feel cold." For the first time her sagacious advice proved wrong. The wind whistled in my well-covered ears something that sounded like, "Go back to your warm apartment." I stopped at a sheltered bus stop, and then kept walking like a person looking for the source of snowflakes, like I used to search for breeding grounds of locust swarms in my childhood.

I arrived in Chinatown, stopping at every sheltered bus stop and telephone booth along the way to warm myself up and stamp the snow off myself. Then I found myself in Little Italy. The road was quiet when suddenly I heard a man in a speeding car using obscene words loudly. I thought it was directed at me, as I was the only person walking in the street. I said nothing, just walked toward the curb not knowing where it would lead me. My eyes became blurry and when I looked toward the street light, the falling snowflakes looked more like fluttering fireflies. At that point, I thought I had gone too far and I felt cold through my nose and my cheekbones. I heard footsteps behind me; I stepped aside to make room, but no one was there.

As the night progressed, the weather turned even colder and the cold wind whipped my face. My enthusiasm for snowflakes collapsed like a house on the African sand. Above all, my fate brought me to Canada to break the age-old contract with poverty that was signed by my ancestors and to face the consequences—artificial or natural. As I approached 118th Avenue, I felt that as if I were at the edge of the world, close to the Arctic. I closed my eyes for a brief moment, imagining as if the Arctic were inside the city of Edmonton. I also imagined myself back home during the same time previous years, looking for relief from sweltering heat and walking around in a sweat stained shirt. Then I decided to return reluctantly, as I always thought to get closer to the sky and heaven was to live in the Arctic.

I thought it was a couple of hours since I left my sister's apartment, but it was more than that. I also remembered that I had an appointment with my ESL classmate from Azerbaijan for a sleepover at his place. Suddenly, I heard an engine of a slowing car behind me, but I turned my head toward the building and walked faster, or pretended to. I was nervous and shaking. I felt like I was followed by gangsters. The car came close to the sidewalk crushing the snowflakes and the windshield wipers moved loudly. The driver lowered his car window leaning across the seat and pushed open the passenger door. I tried to walk as quickly as I could and keep away from the car. The driver called my name with an accent I was familiar with. The driver was my Azeri friend with my sister in the back seat.

To my surprise, they found me. My sister was happy, but also angry. I knew I left around 6:30 or 7, but she told me it was 11.

"What are you doing at this time of the night in this neighbourhood? You have only been here for a few weeks. This place is far away from where we belong."

I was quite thankful that my friend did not understand our conversation in our native language, as I had always hated showing my weak points or difficulties.

"I don't blame you," he assured me, when I finished my conversation with my sister.

"But don't worry, I'll not tell our classmates on Monday."

I smiled at him, as I felt like a rescued animal. When my friend stopped his car in front of the building, I politely declined his invitation and decided to follow my sister.

When my sister unlocked the door, her husband was reading a week-old newspaper that I brought from school. He said nothing, as if he did not notice my return. I felt unwelcome and went to my room. My room was so quiet—no noisy rain gutter or pattering of rain drops—as the snowflakes had quietly landed on the roof of the building.

The exciting restless night was too long, as I slept little and woke up often. In the morning I met my sister in her kitchen where she dropped a couple of slices in the toaster. I ate my breakfast and hurriedly put on my winter dress. Outside, unlike my African village's dark mud, the ground was covered with white snow. I watched leafless trees as they hosted icicles like winter fruits. I was elated and wore the expression of a fascinated child, but I kept my mouth shut to protect my teeth from the bitter cold. If I were a woman, I would have danced and ululated.

A JOINING

AUDREY SHIELD

Even in winter, it catches you by the throat. Occasionally before first
snowfall, there is a thin time when you can skate the bends of creeks.
Along the banks,
the frozen water
curves smooth and clear enough to see minnows swimming
beneath skates.

There are stories there.
Trails of bubbles locked at different depths.
Leaves captured as they spiraled.
The passing of a deer is written in cobalt shadow,
marked when new ice
crumpled.

Along the bank,
white spruce tower
forty feet in the air. Skittering across the cold surface,
their stiff brown cones laugh.

In early winter, the day vanishes swiftly into twilight. Azure into indigo.
Lapis into navy. The blueness of sky deepens and grows in richness as
moon lifts in the east. Stillness quickens. The world holds its breath.

Into the darkening, our skates slice long lines. You warm
our small daughter's hands in your large ones and the ice cracks,
shoots sound running through the smooth clear surface
for almost a mile.
Some undefined joy shouts out. This is here.

SALAMANDER

JASON LEE NORMAN

Things I know about salamanders:

Last year my brother and some of his coworkers found a salamander near a park that they were building. They did what most people would do and they stopped working for the day and took the salamander with them. They took it to a pet store and showed the woman at the pet store what they had. The woman at the pet store told them that it was a salamander. She said you almost never see salamanders this far north. My brother bought a tank for it and some fake rocks and fake plants. The woman at the store told him to buy some live crickets. That's what salamanders eat, she said. So he bought some live crickets that came in a little plastic tub and bought a fake coconut thing that you could turn upside down and make a little home for the salamander.

A long time ago people used to think that salamanders lived in fire. Muslims used to believe that salamanders were literally representations of the devil. Salamanders would hide and sleep in old logs and when people would collect logs to burn in their fireplaces they would sometimes take logs that salamanders were sleeping in. The logs would burn in the fireplace and then the people would see a salamander scurry out of the burning log. This is why people used to think that salamanders lived in fire.

Last month my brother went out of town and I had to babysit the salamander. He brought the tank and the tub of crickets and the fake coconut over to my house and every two days we had to feed the salamander some crickets. Every day my brother was away we worried that the salamander would die. We checked in on it at all hours of the day and night and it never moved once unless it was time to feed it crickets. It stayed in its coconut house. Once we thought we saw it swimming in the little water dish but when we turned the light on to get a better look he was back inside his coconut house. Some people might say that salamanders are boring, but I wouldn't go that far.

Leonardo da Vinci said that the only thing salamanders could eat was fire. The Chinese believed that salamanders slept in fire and then would weave cocoons that the Chinese would then unravel and use to make armour out of. They called it salamander wool. This fabric was so fire resistant, like asbestos, and the only way to clean it was to throw in into a fire and all the dirt would burn off and the cloth would remain clean. The real reason that people believed all these things about salamanders was because the salamander's body was so cold. Ice cold. So cold that it would freeze your hand if you ever picked it up (I never once picked up my brother's salamander). I wasn't afraid that it would be too cold. I was afraid that it would wriggle away and get lost in the house somewhere and then die behind a dresser or something and then my brother would get mad that we couldn't even babysit one little salamander properly. A long time ago word started to get around about these little creatures that were so cold to touch. In the winter they'd hibernate in fallen logs and then awaken once the logs were thrown in a fireplace, thus creating the legend that salamanders were born in fire. Then people started to believe that salamanders could control fire and that they even consumed it to stay alive.

I know people who are salamanders. They hide in their coconut houses all winter and only come out to eat crickets. They do their best impressions of a hibernating animal. They are just like that salamander that I babysat last month. They do nothing and aren't very fun to be around.

I also know people who are like that other kind of salamander; the kind that myths started to form around. People that are cold and live in this cold city and the only thing they have to combat the cold with is fire. Maybe not literal fire (please don't set yourselves on fire to combat the cold weather. Ever). They take the opposite of their extreme cold circumstance and use it to fight off the things that nature is trying to make them feel. The need to hibernate, to gather food to last all winter, those short days and long nights that make you want to just sleep inside your coconut house. They fight that urge to slow their body clocks down with the desire to create things and to make music and to be around one another. These are the people who you see smiling while shivering at the bus stop and the people at the skating rink with big red rosy clown cheeks because they've spent so much time outdoors.

I want us to become a city of salamanders. I want us to fight the cold with fire and I want us to live in it and consume it. I want us to become a city that is invigorated by how cold our bodies feel sometimes. I want people to start their cars at six in the morning when it's 40 below and in that moment before the key turns the ignition I want them to realize that the frozen silence that has been trapped in that car all night is like a blank page, filled with opportunity. I want it to invigorate us so much that a myth starts to grow about our power. People will see us walking down the street and they'll think that the clouds from our exhalations are smoke from the fire we've just consumed. The myth will grow so large that people will start to believe that we are the only ones who know how to truly be warm. People will come from miles around and they'll ask us how they can be warm too. They'll come from places where it's never cold like Ecuador and Greece and they'll ask us where the fire comes from.

And we'll show them.

WHAT THE EARTH HOLDS

CARLA MAJ

I'd met his grandfather, Michael, once before at Michael's home in Watrous, Saskatchewan. His skin was grey even then, made more ashen by the haze of cigarette smoke that wrapped around all of us like thick December clouds. We were all there that day, sitting on counters and laps, leaning against walls, perched on windowsills, crowding around the square metal table, swigging Molson, clanging bottles, belching furiously. The smoke was harsh in my nose and it burned, and I was relieved to get a scent of the men now and the musty and stale, the smell of manure, the smell of rust, the smell hard work and few comforts.

Michael was my husband's grandfather. His wife, Winnie, had just died of complications from diabetes, and my husband, who just happened to be standing over her at the hospital the afternoon she died, had watched her heave and gasp like a beached, silver whale before she was dead. Now my husband had come home from Alberta to be with Michael and the family. Although it seemed to us like Winnie's body was still warm enough to soften the dirt, the ground in December was too frozen to accept her body, and they would just have to wait for southern winds to thaw the edge of town.

They found Michael that February after Winnie passed on, slumped against an elm tree in the yard, one hand in the front of his button-up shirt, Napoleon-style, knobbed with frosted knots, and the other wedged in the left pocket of his pants. His feet were worse off, stiff in his boots, wooden. When they took his socks off, they found a mass of purple blisters, and by the way they were described by some people who talked to some people who saw them, or feet just like them, they must have looked something like raw turnips, rotting.

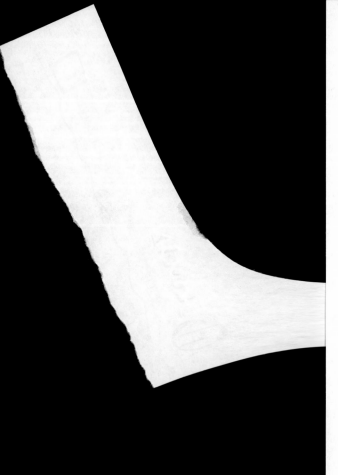

It wasn't the cold that killed him, we heard later, but a heart attack big enough to suffocate his reason, make him stumble from the kitchen, throw the screen door wide open and leave it swinging from its hinges in the wind until the steady banging brought the neighbour over close to midnight.

Once the Amens had been said and the tuna finger sandwiches devoured, we swore we'd never go back there, and we never have. Winter is hardly different in Alberta now, but even when the ground is as frozen as an ice rink in January, the snow here doesn't bury our dead. Under the elm tree in our backyard lays a row of small, heart-shaped tulip bulbs planted by our three boys before the first snow. Nestled in their small, earthen cradles, the bulbs wait for the slow-burning prairie sun to reveal the beauty always pulsing at their core; beauty that is colour, that is warmth, that is life just waiting to be born.

THE MORNING WE CREAKED ON SQUARE WHEELS TO CAMPUS

CAROL MACKAY

We are library folk huddled among metal dangers in the tongue-skinned stacks. We circulate survivalism, Freud, love poetry, Cooking with Hot Peppers, sex and its joys. The A/V guy says we'd be screwed if the power went out. Like popsicles. Frost-bit strawberries. Sweet, sweet ice crystal cream.

We warm by the coffee maker with a few airline bottles but his rosebud pitch is shattered into shards by a Technical Services sniper; a cataloguer, labeller, protector of the physical book and all that is normal. Brown bottles back in the cupboard. This is normal, they remind us.

We do not call in olive-drabs. We do not freeze to death in left coast yoga pants and short sleeves. We are the overdressed heartland and it shall remain so; today is our finest.

After the sniper has gone back to his corner office to alarm-strip his books, we pull out leisure paperbacks to read aloud; one Scoville-rated paragraph after another. Red Sevina, Devil Toung, Madame Jeanette, to raise the temperature so any danger can pass.

HOLDING ON AT WINTER'S EDGE

DANIELLE METCALFE-CHENAIL

I flick the leaves
Clinging to December
Wondering how some hold on so long
And others fall to
Whims of winds
And winter shakedowns
Brought down
To ground's height
Under a slight snow

Snow underfoot
Boots grinding
Picking their way
Trying not to fall
Into the violence
Of in-between seasons
Trying not
To succumb to thoughts
Held under the river's ice

EVENING

DANIELLE METCALFE-CHENAIL

I slipped into the ice fog
Coating myself
With denser air
My hand burning from the doorknob

The lights kept me lonely
As I walked through snow
Punishing my lungs
With ice-tipped air
The ravens just stared
Straddling streetlights
Their backs heavy with frost

WINTER STORIES LIKE YOUR GRANDPARENTS TELL YOU

DANIELLE PARADIS

This story always makes me sound closer to eighty-five than twenty-five. I grew up like the first wanderers into the West, and it's made me hate the cold a lot.

But   When I was very young my family moved around. I was too young to know why we moved.

And   The simplest answer is that my parents chased their dreams and their youth. They seemed to live from moment-to-moment in an adolescent joy with confidence boosted by marijuana and the romanticization of country life.

But   Even grown, adults can't always understand their parents' actions.

And   We lived once in a summer cabin in the winter. There was a wood stove that kept us alive.

But   Never really warm all the way through.

And   I had nightmares. We lived on Hubbles Lake and in my dreams a giant lobster monster would crawl from the icy depths, and cut up my binoculars

But   That dream never did make any sense.

And   We moved when I was six to a couple of ATCO trailers on a plot of land that my mom and stepdad had purchased to build their dream home.

But Dreams take time. There were two separate cabins—a sleeper and one with a kitchen. When you woke up you'd have to rush from one to the other hoping someone else had turned on the furnace. The bathroom was an outhouse. We tied string along a path so you could find it in the dark.

And We moved into a half-built house. The walls were up and the insulation was in. I learned not to touch it or else angry bumps would rise on my skin.

But We still didn't have heat, so we used propane torches and space heaters—because we did have power.

And Not long after that I went to live with my Grandmother.

But I never got to love the cold. I feel a chill pretty easily and I'll never understand why people want to go outside and freeze their asses off.

And I prefer my yuppie winter coat, short walks from the bus to the office, and extra-hot overpriced lattes.

SIRENS

DIANA DAVIDSON

None of her lullabies work. She soothes and rocks, sings and cradles, caresses her new baby with little result. He cries and fusses and won't fall asleep; the only thing that lessens the crying is when she bounces him against her body. She can't even go outside for a change of scenery. The sun hangs in the afternoon sky like bait on a fishing line. There is a deep freeze in Edmonton and more snow is projected for tonight. She is not supposed to shovel yet, it hasn't been six weeks since the C-section, and she is terrified of slipping on the ice while holding the baby and not being able to pull herself up. Her days are spent trapped inside a little house.

It's her third winter here and it is much colder than the first or second. Her first winter in Edmonton she could feel surprise at how her breath froze in the air, she could see the beauty of Christmas lights peeking through the snow-laden branches of a spruce tree, she could find warmth by a fire with a cup of tea. But now, this winter, she feels it deep in her body: her hip bones ache, her pelvis is an empty cradle of cold, her mind can't settle. Her husband tells her she feels this way because she isn't sleeping, she's nursing a newborn, she's just had surgery, and she shouldn't be so hard on herself. But something is stopping her from feeling the way she should. And she wishes she could get the baby to stop crying so much.

It's evening now. She feels relief as she hears the silver key turn in the door. Her husband is finally home. He might succeed in comforting their child. Besides an occasional night time interruption when their son cries for her milk, his routine hasn't changed. He still sleeps most of the night, gets up in the morning, showers, gets dressed, eats his breakfast with both hands, drives to work, grabs a latte and interacts with other adults until he comes home for supper.

She suspects he doesn't believe her that the little one screams and squirms in her arms most of the day; the baby always seems to settle when he gets home. Their son loves the sound of his father's voice saying "Hi baby boy, hello …."

Tonight, she decides, will be different. After her husband takes off his fleece-lined boots and hangs up his puffy red eiderdown, before he can say "Oh, those Christmas decorations are still up" and tentatively ask, "How was your day?," she hands him the baby and says, "He's just been fed and changed. I'm going to have a bath."

"Okay," he replies, surprised by her decisive tone. "When you're done, I'll need to go out and shovel the walks. It's snowing again."

She nods. She leaves them and locks herself in the bathroom. She takes off the pajama pants and stained t-shirt she's been wearing for two days. The clothes crumple onto a cold tile floor like skin of a gutted fish. She smells of sour milk, baby powder, and nervous sweat. She looks in the dirty mirror and tries to recognize herself. The leaking breasts, tangled hair, deflated stomach, and angry red scar below her belly button seem to belong to someone else. She is a foreigner in her own skin.

The first week or so, things were alright. Their son was born a day before New Year's Eve and they came home from the hospital on the first of January. Everything was new. She marvelled at how her son's tiny head fit in the palm of her hand. She loved the way he smelled of softness and warmth and purpose. She and her husband stared at his tiny hands and changed their minds hourly about whose nose or ears he had inherited. She came to know the mewing sounds he made as he woke up between naps. She loved how he tried to make himself small as she held him against her skin, in the crook of her arms, at her breast. She sang songs to him—every song she knew: carols about heralding angels and Jesus in a manger, nursery rhymes about sailors who go to sea, folk songs about women who go to the market with red flowers in their hair. She felt the things she was supposed to feel.

Then, one Sunday morning when the baby was nearly two weeks old, she woke up from a few hours sleep and things seemed different. The snowfall was suffocating, the baby's cries were a failure rather than an indicator, her husband didn't understand. He suggested that they all bundle up and get out of the house and go for a coffee. But it didn't help. It seemed to be an insurmountable task to decide how many diapers to put in the diaper bag and what blanket to use in the car seat. The vehicle's tires gripped at icy intersections and she braced herself for them to crash even though there was no one else on the road. Once they got to the coffee shop, her husband told her to find a table and take some deep breaths. She put the baby, still in his car seat, on the table and pulled up a chair. Her husband brought over two coffees. She tried. She wanted for them to sit quietly in the wood-and-iron warmth of this cafe as the baby slept and share a moment. She wanted to look out the window and see the falling snow as beautiful. She wanted to be able to watch it cascade and swirl and blanket the world in its cool white ambivalence. She wanted, for a moment, to feel that it was only them, only this, and that everything was alright. But it wasn't. A stranger's interruption to coo at her sleeping baby in his car seat, the hiss of steam from the espresso machine, even KD Lang crooning "Miss Chatelaine": all these sounds seemed to really be whispers of 'danger, danger—you are not good enough.' Even the green siren on her paper coffee cup seemed to grin at her in a malicious way. She just wanted to go home as soon as she left the house. She wanted to leave; she wanted to be somewhere where it wasn't winter, where it was warm.

That afternoon, her husband took down the Christmas tree while she wept, silently, on the couch and the baby slept in his bassinet. He tried to comfort her. He said things like, "Lots of new mothers go through this," and "It's the hormones," and "You just need a good night's sleep" but none of that was quite right. She felt bad; she knew he was trying. She watched as her husband put away the crimson ribbons and gold stars and tiny bells. He left some things out: candles that look as if they are wrapped in bark, a winding branch of plastic red berries, and four silver deer that graze the mantle above the gas fireplace in their living room. These deer are liquid and graceful and shimmering. They are frozen in their clean silver beauty.

Tonight, she slips into a tub dangerously full to the brim and lets the chrome tap run nearly scalding. She wants to burn the cold and sweat and fear off her skin. She wants water that isn't frozen ice or a suffocating snow drift. She puts her big toe into the silver faucet and lets the water run down her foot. She tries to quiet her mind. She can't hear the baby crying so her husband must be succeeding where she's failed.

She sinks into the water. This morning she listened to a man on CBC radio talking about polar bears and how they wandered into his village in Nunavut looking for food. The man's voice was sad. He talked about how there was less of everything: fewer ice floes, fewer seals, and fewer caribou as everything warmed. What struck her was her own helplessness: what could she do about the crumbling world she's just brought a baby into? She should drive less, recycle more, give more to charities whose supporters chain themselves to trees and write manifestos about the oil sands. What if a polar bear came prowling around their yard looking for supper? Do polar bears come as far south as Edmonton? She has no idea. She doesn't have a gun as her husband doesn't hunt. She can't even get her baby to stop crying let alone protect him from displaced predators. Soon, maybe, the coasts will erode, the arctic will disintegrate, and they will all be under water. Perhaps her son will not have to worry because none of this will matter.

She sinks deeper into the tub and imagines she is diving into the ocean's belly. She can taste salty water filling her nostrils and mouth. Her skin feels slippery. She wants to be quick and silver and liquid. She feels called to go deeper. She closes her eyes and sees waves crash against the shore. She wants the opposite of hard, cold, whiteness. With each watery breath, she lets go a little bit more. She finally starts to feel warm.

"Honey!" Her husband has been knocking for a least a minute and he is getting frantic. "Honey— open the door. I need to know you're okay."

She comes back. She lets her nose push through the surface of the water. She waits a moment and then slowly gets out of the tub. She ignores what is happening on the other side of the door. She stands on the plush green bath mat and watches water run from her torso down her thighs, over her knees and shins, and pool between her unpainted toes.

She reaches into her husband's shaving kit and pulls out a small silver blade. It makes a neat red line across the inside of her wrist. It starts to pulse warm and red.

Her husband pushes open the door with his body, breaking the flimsy silver lock. She stands there, naked and dripping, her long black hair brushing the tops of her sore and cracking nipples, her wrist bleeding onto the green bath mat. He stares at her for a moment and then grabs the First Aid kit from its place under the sink and finds gauze to quickly wrap around her wound.

"Hold your arm up," he says.

She does.

"I didn't realize …," he whispers. He takes a blue fluffy towel from the shelf and wraps it around her nakedness. She wonders if he has imagined this possibility on his drive home from work. She wonders if he has lingered in the parking lot or taken a longer route home fearing he would find something like this.

"Why would you do this?" he asks her softly.

She is silent.

He pulls her close, into him, and she goes limp like a fish.

"The baby's asleep. I'm calling an ambulance. It's going to be okay."

Her husband strokes her wet hair.

She is silent.

"The hospital will know how to help you."

She watches the blood soak through the white gauze on her wrist.

"Keep holding your arm up. You will be okay."

He sits her on the bath mat. She's never noticed that it is the colour of seaweed.

"Stay right there, don't move. We will be okay."

She waits to hear the wail of the ambulance. She imagines its red lights flashing, glistening under the wave of falling snow. She wishes she were still under the water.

NARCISSUS

DONIA MOUNSEF

In the ice kingdom
rivers sleep in winter
hibernate under blocks of cracked ice
dreaming of warmth and wild runs
to the other side of the great divide
scraping glacial deposits to the Hudson Bay
they rest their chary beds until spring
when they open their eyes
awakened by the gods of the tundra
jet under the surface
tickling the frozen mass from beneath

the south bank of the North Saskatchewan River
is a tropical garden
a green ribbon where one finds
in the dead of winter a northern maidenhair fern
veiled in darkness wrestling with the northern light
in a barren winter poplar
a strident reverberation of a magpie
watching over its empty nest
stretches its white noise over the taciturn valley

stop to look at a strange plant
with green leaves frozen in the shape of an origami raven
wings etched into the ice blanket
wintery eyes spot something moving under the surface
a liquid kaleidoscope waiting to be reunited with solid matter
gaze at the glassy sheet
become a Narcissus
bent down to kiss a water vision
an emergent image falls into you
plaintive, it whispers like Echo for eternity

repeating words spoken into the undying gorge
yearning for love that would never be returned

where the body disappeared
a flower is painfully trying to grow in its place

SNOW

DONIA MOUNSEF

Thirty one words for snow
the first people of this land have
Niggiut – snowdrift
Aniuk – snow for drinking
Kavisilaq – snow brick to build igloos
Masak – wet snow
Aput – snow on the ground
Maujaq – deep soft snow where it is hard to walk
Piqsiq – snow in a blizzard
Uluarnaq – round snowflakes

packed
iced
blasted
powdered
weighing down oak branches
soundless particles
night limps behind footsteps
leading to nowhere
holed by a bold boot on feeble feet
a moon hidden
inside intersecting night clouds
dancing on your hand
like an arctic wave
fluttering a hesitant wind
sifting through words
what if our whole life
we always chose the wrong language

I practice guttural sounds to stay warm
inhale the burdensome cold
exhale the icy glow of emerald pain
track shapes made by frozen breath

a faded picture in liquid form
a body sketch in the snow
an idea trickles
like frozen water
flowing to unseen gutters
beneath a city unsure of its identity
between the quick blackness of smokestacks
and the long survival of coniferous green

a fist clenched frozen shut
on a perfect pebble
pilfered from a distant sea
half the globe away
where memory of warm sand
sways you in the eyelids of the gods
a blanket woven from refugee fingers
I have thrown over you
a drop of sweat melting the white surface
lit up inside you my lust
a frozen flame
a declaration of hunger
for your nakedness
in the thickness of winter
layers become a list of grievances
growing inside us like an ocean quake

a lingering scent of sex
on gloved fingers
a question unanswered
lost in the acoustic of white silence
the glacial land speaks a different language
I am not certain I understand
in the snow a yes is often a no
so now
now
so no

WINDCHILL

DONIA MOUNSEF

I

You grow to like the open prairie
with its blanket of white powder
its endless nights, its foolish sun
"foolish, fake, phony, false
a mockery, pretend, the sun here is a sham"
the old Lebanese lady warned the newcomer
because it shines bright but cannot warm your heart

learn to appreciate the howling wind
over the terra firma
Apollonian
push back against Dionysian mountains
boundaries to organize the chaos of difference
shackles on the ankles of a hunter's freedom
gaze at its smokestacks
elevators to the heavens
where oil executives in white crisp shirts and sober ties
dream to ascend with their SUVs and bailout cash in tow

II

You trace the northern lights with your index finger
stare at an inner sea to find your bearing
following a secret coastline
the aerial formation
of a lone Swainson's hawk
soaring the gaping sky
diving to catch a mouse not of hunger but of fear of stillness
practice telling temperature
with a wet finger in mid air
sensing digital barometric readings
atmospheric pressure
with or without windchill

the factor that differentiates truth from fable
pleasure from pain
dream of huddling with your fellow northerners
around an imaginary fire
drink cognac with their shadows
borrow their warm skin
slip into it like a coverall
but it glides off your coral snapper scales

III

You learn to speak the silence of the flat land
where language is frozen in icy luggage
where love poems are frostbites
made of sheets of snow and wind
stitched together by the arthritic hand of an aging farmer
derelict words lie in abandoned heaps
dirty snow in deserted parking lots
pebbles to be picked up
dusted off like rare seashells
warmed up in the palm of your hand
stuffed in your pocket

IV

You look for the end of this earth
but the flat land is limitless
it circles around your soul
like a moth to the flame
from a dying body
it steals a breath
and sends it north
to freeze under the tundra

from a somnolent gaze
it steals a frozen glow
and sends it south
to unthaw in tropical heat

from a frozen hand
it steals a pinch of dust
and sends it west
to scatter over a forgotten sea

from a broken heart
it steals a silent beat
and sends it east
to pulsate the torn skin of a lost drum

MONTMARTRE, EDMONTON

ERIKA LUCKERT

Two river cities: I put Paris over Edmonton and try to see through the paper—the North Saskatchewan and the Seine crossing each other and merging. I pick out a thumbtack—*rouge*—place its point at Montmartre, and press it through both maps. Then, I tear away the Parisian page, leaving only the map of Edmonton. The thumbtack marks my destination.

I like to go looking for a story—to map my way towards a plot and, in navigating, find myself in the middle of it. When I was in Paris, I took the metro to Montmartre, and, fittingly, my Edmonton route takes me on the LRT. I wait ten minutes for the train, knowing that in Paris, three would have passed in that time. While I wait, a man approaches me, wants to know the time (ten to two, or *quatorze heures moins dix*), and asks to buy a train ticket from me for $1.75. I turn him down—"I only have a pass," I say. When travelling, I've been taught to keep my wallet hidden, and politely decline any requests made by unknown men: *non, désolée.*

At the point of the red thumbtack, there's a small playground half-buried in snow. There are children playing despite the cold, and one says hello. I reply in English, and try to translate the playground landscape to Parisian places that I know. The monkey bars, unused in this weather, are the market stalls, where silk scarves, purses, and flowing skirts might hang. In Montmartre, navigating through those stalls, there are throngs of people—offering *petit tour Eiffels* on key chains, insisting that you stop to have your portrait drawn—*trop belle, mademoiselle*. Here, the few children save their breath—the cold has a way of silencing, of making space. I find a space on the park bench, brushing aside the snow, and perch on the icy surface below. I write with mittened hands and try to warm myself with the thought of a little café in France, but the park is noticeably lacking in hot beverages, so after a few more minutes, I stand up to leave. In Paris, I could be no more than a block from a warm *café* at any time, but I know that in Edmonton, I would be lucky to find a hot drink in walking distance. Still, the thought of writing indoors with a steaming mug is enough to make me try. Numbing feet take me along the gridded streets to a larger road, and *heureusement,* just three blocks away, I find "The End Zone Pub and Grill."

Two men stand outside the door, smoking, their exhales dramatic in the chilly air. I pick my seat by the window, and a few minutes later, they come inside. They traverse the pub with a familiarity that reminds me I am a foreigner here; as they take six easy steps from the door to the bar, I see that the dark carpet is worn pale along their path.

I order a hot chocolate (*chocolat chaud,* I say to myself), and a small soup: chicken noodle. The hot chocolate is made from a mix, but they've stirred it well, and besides, it's warm. I start to write.

The stereo plays some kind of thumping pop, the sort of thing that was popular in France when I was there. "You're so beautiful, so damn beautiful," goes the refrain. They listen to English music in Paris too—it's *très cool.*

One of the men from outside sits down at the next table. His jacket is faux leather, worn enough that it could almost pass for real. After a few sentences, he turns, and asks me what I'm writing.

"A story," I say.

"What's it about?"

"It's a travel story," I decide. "About Paris." Is that a lie?

He asks me if I've been to Paris, and I tell him yes, and when he asks what it's like, I make a comment about the weather. I don't tell him that, in a way, I'm in Paris right now. That I'm within walking distance of the *Moulin Rouge.* That really, so is he.

We talk for a while—the conversation of strangers, the first words you learn in any foreign language. Not "where is the bathroom," but "my name is Erika, *comment t'appelles tu*?" He asks about school, about what I'll do next. I tell him I'll probably go down to the states to study. It's a good idea, he thinks. "Up here in Canada, we need priests, but down there, they need people like you." I'm not sure about the accuracy of his market analysis, but I agree anyways. When I reach the bottom of my hot chocolate, wet powder clings to the mug—I was wrong, I suppose, about it being well-stirred.

My soup arrives in a Styrofoam bowl—"Sorry for the wait"—and the man offers me some advice about writing. "Live it, learn it, and make it exciting." It sounds good to me, and he adds, "Don't leave out the sex scenes." I laugh, and he raises his beer. "Cheers." I think that those words will be the last line of my story, so I start thinking of French translations—*chin, santé, à la votre, salut*—but he turns around to speak to me again.

"So did you fall in love out there?" He's talking about Paris. When I tell him no, he continues.

"What are your likes and dislikes? I mean, what are your tastes in men?"

I'm taken aback and, awkwardly, I mention my boyfriend. He laughs. "I'm just flirting, that's all."

I laugh too, relieved that it's been made explicit. He adds, "You're beautiful, you know?" and I think of France, and the song that was playing when I came in. So damn beautiful.

"I'm single," he says, "but I would marry you in a heartbeat."

He goes back to his beer, and I try the soup that's been cooling as we talked. I write with one hand, hold the spoon with the other, and when I'm about halfway through, the man gets up to leave, giving me a nod on the way out. I watch him walk out into the cold and across the street before turning back to my notebook. After a few more lines, I decide to leave the last chunks of chicken in the bottom of the Styrofoam bowl.

YOU COUNT TIME BY THE CARS PASSING BY

ERIN OTTOSEN

You count time by the cars passing by as you walk the secluded stretch of road that dips down deep into the ravine. So inviting during the day, so you decided to walk it at night in a heavy snowfall, a heavy snowfall that's falling on top of another heavy snowfall that's made the world look like marshmallows on whipped cream. The snow reflecting on snow brightens the night, makes the sky a deep warm velvety blue. You'll go home in the deep velvety blue.

You trudge down into the dip, ever closer to the bottom of the ravine and the cradle where the creek sleeps. Your feet slide constantly in the ever-shifting snow, and the houses drop underneath the horizon as the ravine rises up around you. The trees and lamp posts grow tall, and the time passes with the cars. When the cars come towards you, their headlights split around the tree trunks and make the falling snow glitter like shooting stars.

There's a footbridge to the side of the road, an elegant footbridge that used to brace trains. It joins hillside to hillside and it would spare you from venturing all the way down and all the way up, but it disappears into trees, into black. So you stay on the road.

If you keep your shoulders still, and if you do not turn your head, there are no cracks in your armour. But when you turn your body to centre on a sound, the cold cuts through your scarf and pricks your neck and shoulders.

The hill stretches out longer with every step you take, and your step is never steady in the ever-shifting snow. And now you're in the cradle. Either side is just as long. There's a numbness spreading through you, your legs slabs, your face wooden. And sometimes, cars pass. They move slowly while the snow falls fast and unrelenting, icing your face, caking your coat. The hill you climb is stretching, stretching out longer with every step you take. The light from the lamp posts are scattered circles, fading. The light from the cars, passing. You're going home in what is now a deep velvety black. So inviting. You decided to walk it. You're alone. Secluded stretch of road. Heavy snowfall. Heavy snow. Alone and lonely in this wondrous world of snow, and you count time by the cars passing by. You count time. And sometimes, time stops.

MEMORIES OF WINTER IN EDMONTON

ESMERALDA CABRAL

I can barely see the mountains on the north shore; they are shrouded in cloud once again. The drizzle lands on my face and leaves droplets on my glasses, and I am unable to see much after a few minutes. I take off my glasses and everything is a blur. Vancouver. After twenty years of living here, I am still not used to the unrelenting December rain and I find myself longing for the Edmonton winters that I once knew. Perhaps my time away allows me to romanticize the snow and cold but what I remember most are the blue skies, the sunny days and the mounds of white fluffy snow. I know it got very cold, and sometimes winter felt like it was way too long but, as I tell anyone who will listen, it is easier to deal with the cold if there is also sunshine.

I loved winter and snow from the moment I arrived in Edmonton. I was seven years old and our family had just emigrated from our island home in the Azores. It was a cold, gray day in September and it was already snowing. The flakes didn't last—they touched the ground and melted into the pavement—but I was mesmerized by the swirling white.

I remember the drive from the airport to my uncle's house in the Londonderry area—I thought the falling snowflakes were the most beautiful things I'd ever seen. The rest of my family was not so enchanted. My father sat in the front passenger seat, in silence. Every once in a while, my uncle would turn to him and say, "Eh, Manuel, what you think?" and my father would tilt his head to one side and shrug his shoulders, and then say, "Long trip. Long trip." My mother sat in the back seat with my sister Maria and me and cried almost the whole way. In between her sobs she asked my uncle, her brother, why he hadn't bothered telling her that there would be snow by the time we arrived.

"It's early this year," he said. "It's not usually like this."

Back home, in Sao Miguel, we could still swim in the ocean in September, sometimes even into October.

Maria tried to make our mother feel better. "This is our new home now, ma, it'll be okay." My mother cried harder and louder. Life in Canada probably did not seem as daunting to Maria since she, at least, could speak English. She was seventeen, and she had learned English and French in high school back home. My parents had taken a few lessons once they knew we'd be emigrating, but they didn't know very much, probably could not even carry on a basic conversation.

We stepped out of the car when we got to my uncle's house and the cold slapped us in the face. All of us stood there, stunned at how cold the cold could be. My aunt and my cousins waited for us inside the house. I had never met them but I ran in first while the others gathered the luggage and brought it inside. Eight suitcases. Two for each of us. It was all that remained of the island we'd left behind.

"Welcome. Welcome to Canada," my aunt said.

We shopped for winter clothes at Woodward's and The Bay, downtown. I remember my first coat, a green fuzzy parka that resembled a shag carpet. It had a hood with white fur trim and drawstrings to bring the fur tight around my face. I also got one of those white furry hats with pom poms on a string to tie up under the chin. It made my head look like I was wearing a helmet from outer space but I loved that hat. It was so soft. I don't remember my boots but they would have had to be warm and comfortable—I walked twelve blocks to my elementary school. In the mornings, I walked with the other school children who lived on my block but after school, they had extracurricular activities and I was on my own. My mother picked me up every day. She was unaccustomed to wearing long pants so she would wear a skirt and two pairs of nylons, and a coat that went to just below her hips. When she would get to the school, her knees would be bright red and she'd need a rest before we would start off on our walk home.

After two weeks at my uncle's house, we moved into our first home—a sparsely furnished house in the Norwood area, where many of Edmonton's 8,000 Portuguese immigrants lived. Some of our neighbours felt badly for us because we knew so little about living in the cold. They lent us hats and scarves and gloves and thick socks because they knew we would need more than just one pair each. As winter progressed, we learned that the cold we had felt on our first day in Edmonton was hardly indicative of the chill that was to come. The winter of 1969 had one of the longest cold snaps on record—the temperature remained at minus twenty or colder for twenty-six days straight.

The fridge in our house had a built-in freezer compartment but it didn't work. It would accumulate ice very quickly and there would be no room to put anything in there. Our landlord didn't see this as an urgent matter so for the entire first winter in that house, we used the snow banks in our back yard to store ice cream, frozen corn, frozen peas and anything else that needed to be kept frozen. The fridge was so small that sometimes we'd put our milk out there too, just to make room in the lower compartment for the rest of our food.

My parents shovelled a lot of snow. Mostly, my mother did it because my father had two jobs and he was at work all the time, it seemed. My mother worked too but when she got home in the afternoon, she'd start dinner and then she'd go outside to shovel the snow. Neighbours brought over additional shovels which meant that Maria and I could help our mother after a big snowfall. When we spent time outside we could feel crystals forming above our lips and on our eyelashes and eyebrows. When we went back in the house, we would have frost around our eyes and our cheeks would be so rosy and we'd laugh because we thought we looked like Santa Claus.

Snow sports were completely foreign to us. When my class went on a sleigh ride at Christmas time, my mother wouldn't let me go because it was at night and she didn't really know what was involved. The school counsellor came to our house to explain things to my parents. She said that she, personally, would take care of me and that I'd be okay. My parents let me go. When I came home I was so excited and I was speaking so fast no one could understand me.

"And there were horses, and they pulled this big wagon and all of us went on it at the same time and we'd get thrown off and then run after the wagon and hop back on and get thrown off again. It was so much fun. And then we got hot chocolate."

My mother didn't think this activity sounded like much fun at all.

I got my first pair of skates when I was in grade eight. It took that long for my mother to feel comfortable with the skate-on-ice thing and still, she worried that I'd fall and crack my head. Our school had an outdoor rink and we'd skate at lunchtime and after school. I loved playing 'crack the whip'. If only my mother had known just how dangerous that game could be. Some kids would fall and hurt themselves badly, then come into class with bloody hands or cuts on their faces. When I was in grade nine, the principal announced that we weren't allowed to play 'crack the whip' anymore.

As an older teenager, my favourite outdoor activity was to go skating at Mayfair Park, which was later renamed Hawrelak Park. I had become a fast skater and I'd do figure eights around the two islands in the arti-ficial lake that was turned into a huge outdoor rink every winter. There was a bonfire on one of the islands where we could go to warm up or there was always the shelter where we could rest indoors with a cup of hot chocolate.

I also loved cross-country skiing on the trails at Hawrelak Park. By the time I was eighteen, I had saved up enough money to buy my own cross-country skis, much to my mother's chagrin. Whenever the con-ditions seemed right, a bunch of friends would get together and we'd go skiing, either at Hawrelak Park or further, sometimes, all the way to Elk Island Park. That would be an all-day outing and my mother was always relieved to see me walk in the front door, unhurt.

My children say that my stories about winter in Edmonton sound exotic. To them, skating involves going to an indoor rink, at public skating times, paying admission fees and skating in circles until the buzzer goes and everyone has to have a rest while the Zamboni makes a few passes, up and down, to smooth the ice.

"It's so different than skating outside," I tell them.

When we go cross-country skiing, we're fortunate to be able to drive about an hour and a half to Cypress Bowl, pay for our day pass and ski on the mountain. It's lovely and there are stunning views up there. But it's a different experience than just driving down to Hawrelak Park, strapping on the boards, and skiing. For free.

I don't shovel snow very often in Vancouver. But I do complain about the rain. And when I do, friends (mostly the ones who were born in Vancouver) will say something like "Oh, but it's better than the white stuff," to which I invariably respond, "Not necessarily."

My memories of the twenty-three winters I spent in Edmonton revolve around the crisp days, the crunchy snow, and the sunshine. Always the sunshine. I think I've forgotten just how cold the cold can be.

SOUTHERN LAMENT

GREGORY RAMSHAW

Please don't tell me that I'm lucky.

I know I'll never have to shovel snow again. I know I'll never have to plug in my car. Heck, I now own a car without a block heater! I'll never have to worry about frostbite, my furnace shutting down, or natural gas bills. Thing is, I never really minded any of these things (well, maybe the frostbite). I like shoveling snow! I'd even shovel my neighbours' walks—not to be neighbourly, mind you, but just because I liked it. I enjoy walking in winter. It makes me feel alive and refreshed and pensive. I've always really liked winter but, more importantly, I've always liked—no, loved—winter in Edmonton. And, now that I live away from the snow—in a place where a snowfall is a biannual novelty, at best—I find that I dearly miss Edmonton's darkest but most wonderful season.

My new neighbours—from winter places like Pittsburgh and Trenton and Akron—we all talk about how great it is to live in a place where there is no winter. Of course, I outwardly agree with them, nodding my head while all along knowing deep down I would like nothing more than to wear my toque (four years, never worn), gloves (worn once, for a non-cold-related activity), and coat (misplaced, due to lack of use). I lie, and I have tried desperately to live that lie—bragging to my Edmonton friends and family about year-round golf and Indian summers that never end—but, really, there are times I'd give most anything to walk through a deserted downtown on a snowy Sunday night, the city silent and barren and ablaze with reflected light of a billion snowflakes.

Of course, I know that I romanticize Edmonton winters. It is lovely and wonderful and magical when one doesn't have to experience it directly. Adam Gopnik's essays about winter note that many of our impressions of winter are as a result of romanticism and modernism—that we can love the winter because we are safely sheltered from it. My shelter comes from mobility and globalization. I moved to a warm-weather location for work, not for sunshine. I'd probably hate winter if I still lived in Edmonton, and would probably have S.A.D. like most of the population. I would be searching Expedia for the best deal to Vegas or Cancun or Jamaica like everyone else in the 780. I would check condo prices in Phoenix. I would want to escape.

But, it is hard not to be romantic about winter in Edmonton. Let me share with you three truths I have learned about winter in Edmonton, from a distance:

- Whisky tastes better in Edmonton because of the cold;
- Winter in Edmonton is the best time to have a short-term relationship;
- Sports and recreation are better in the winter.

To explain my first truth, I hate whisky—except in Edmonton, and only when it is very cold. Returning to Gopnik, he contends that modernity has placed a window—both literal and figurative—between us and winter, and that winter becomes a magical, mystical wonderland when we can escape it. Alcohol is an escape, as are public places that serve alcohol. I challenge you, dear Edmontonian, to take a long walk—at least an hour, maybe longer—through your city one cold, winter evening. Then, enter your favourite pub or tavern and order a whisky (I shall leave the location and the brand up to you). Finish said whisky quickly, and soak up the juxtaposition between the whisky and your walk. I guarantee this ritual to make you feel both enamoured with your city and your fellow barfly.

As to the second truth, it has been many years since I have had a winter relationship in Edmonton (love you, Honey!). However, I do believe that winter in Edmonton makes for the best flings. To begin, there is a talent to being both fashionable and warm in Edmonton. Someone once explained to me that, during winter in Edmonton, it is difficult to make an "entrance"—there is an egalitarian leveler to the winter that makes it damn near impossible to step out during the winter months.

Thus, one has to be rather creative to brave the elements and put on a show. Creativity is sexy.

I also think that, though summer flings in Edmonton can be good fun (again, love you Honey!), they lack the depth of winter relationships. Summer relationships are based on the four-four time of a Gas Pump-esque soundtrack; winter relationships are built on a certain depth, shared sacrifice, and warm, wonderful blankets. Winter flings are situated in discussions of Sartre, driving the other to your place because his (or her) car won't start, going to a friend's play about death and coal mining as a starting point to an evening's lovemaking. Indeed, these relationships may—and often, do—inevitably end as the siren of summer skin comes calling. But, one is richer for the winter's experience—indeed, perhaps, it becomes more of a fond memory than those sunshine hook-ups of summer.

Finally, as cliché as it is to link Edmonton with sport, there is something about playing shinny at a community league rink or skating at the Victoria Park oval or cross-country skiing in the River Valley (mind you, I've never actually cross-country skied, though I imagine it to be a wonderful slice of Edmonton recreation). Even watching sports in the winter holds a certain romanticism. To explain, I was—for far too short a time, in my view—a season ticket holder for a team that recently relocated to the Manitoba capital. Walking into or out of the arena when it was warm outside was disconcerting—like the ritual should not be (and, as it turned out, was not). In fact, one of the few times it felt like home was a mid-season game, just after Christmas, a few years ago. It was decently cold—-15°C-ish, enough to make it authentic—and it actually felt like Edmonton. Fact is, the outside temperatures make the indoor ritual all the more powerful. You should have to wipe snow off of your car after the game. Anything else is just roller hockey.

What of my life, then, in the sunshine and perpetual seventy-two degrees (sorry, twenty-two Celsius)? Why can't one be happy in such an environment? Indeed, there are moments of joy, of bliss, and of contentment. The proverbial four horsemen are not exactly at the door. One can drink whisky and watch hockey and engage in romantic entanglements. There is, indeed, something to be said about being able to wear shorts until November and begin again in February. Still, there is a level of artifice that comes with warmer climes. And, dare I say, with hardship comes depth. Without winter, there is no joy in summer. There have been many gorgeous days here when I have eschewed the outdoors, knowing that tomorrow…and tomorrow…and tomorrow would be exactly the same. Why bike or run or walk or sit on a patio today when there is no urgency?

And, I suppose, because the Edmonton summers are glorious—but brief—and because the winter is something you cope with, endure, and share, there is something I miss of that sense of community, of shared sacrifice, of poetry. Edmonton winters are more than just a nostalgia for me, they are part of who I am, and they are something I'd like to share. I now have a son, born into this no-snow-shoveling culture. I want him to skate outdoors on Christmas afternoon, all runny-nosed and ruddy-cheeked when he returns home. I want him to own a set of booster cables, an ice scraper, and a pair of sturdy Sorels. More than this, though, I want him to do this in Edmonton. I want him to feel the cold during the Remembrance Day ceremonies at the City Hall cenotaph. I hope for him to know the beauty of the River Valley after a thick frost. I wish for him to try Purple City during a snowfall. I have no doubt he will form wonderful memories here of autumn tailgating and football, hot summers and freaky insects. I'm sure he'll form a nostalgia for his life here, and no doubt it will include something of his environment. Still, it is not something I can teach him—and, after all, imparting knowledge is half of fun of having children—as we will both be learning this foreign location at the same time.

So, dear Edmontonians, please don't think of me as lucky. There are surface benefits of my new environment, true, but they are only surface. I miss the intensity of Edmonton. I miss the crunch of new snow, the endlessness of the winter, and the anticipation of spring. I miss the walks and the whisky. I miss the skating, the snowshoeing, and the stolen, frozen kisses. Most of all, I miss creating more of these memories, and wish my boy could be more than a midwinter tourist in his father's hometown.

WILD ICE

JAN MCGREGOR

There was one bright shaft of light that shone through the gloom of our Novembers in Edmonton—the hope of Wild Ice. Ice that would tighten across Whitemud Creek and the ponds in the gravel pits in what is now Hawrelak Park and freeze into shimmering transparent glass, glinting shards of sunlight and calling for skates. Perfection only happened about one year in five—ice mirror-smooth and clear enough to see minnows and water-boatman right under your eyes as you lay stretched out face down with your jacket getting gently damp, nose on the ice and hands cupped around your eyes so you could peer into the wonderland of a miniature world only inches away.

In early November the ice would be too frail to walk or lie on; then we would skim small stones across the thin skin and it would respond with a high pitched sibilant song echoing and repeating long after the stone had stopped. Or our first tentative footsteps would send arrows of sound as the ice cracked and moved. We would lie on the ice, ears pressed to the surface and listen to the haunting whale-like singing as a friend walked on it, sometimes hundreds of yards away.

We started hunting for wild ice in early November. We were determined to find it before Nov 11 and meet my father's perpetual dedication to skate on Remembrance Day. Edmonton was colder then, and there were only a few years when he could not skate on wild ice. Mind you, there were several years when my mother would cluck protestations looking at the scant inch of ice as my father laced into his long-bladed speed skates and absolutely forbid us kids to even think of venturing more than three feet from shore. My father's theory was that if you moved fast enough, even thin ice would hold. And he was fast and as smooth as silk, sailing out with long graceful strides, the tympanic ice singing and ringing like a violin plucked by his skates. Most years his theory would prove right, and he would skim around the pond a few times, then drift swiftly back to shore and, without slowing, run onto the land, changing from a soaring tern to a penguin stumbling on the shore. Most years, that was. I remember a few, when his pack would hold a few pairs of dry socks and extra long johns, and we would light a fire on shore before his skates would go on. But on they would go, and out he would glide, circling close to shore until we could just catch an instantaneous glimpse of the ice sagging under him before it would crack, and down he would go, arms outstretched to grab the ice as he fell. My mother's clucking would escalate, we kids would burst out laughing and we'd dance on the shore as my father, usually only knee-deep in mud and water, would break the ice ahead of him until he emerged, dripping muddy slime and long strands of water weeds. His teeth would be chattering almost as loud as Mum's "I told you so"s and "What an idiotic thing to do!"s and "My God, Doug, won't you ever learn!"s. We'd help pull his skates and dripping socks off as he reached his bluish-white hands to the fire. A nip into the bushes to put on the dry long johns and dry socks, then he'd grin and agree that perhaps we should head for home.

Some years the November temperatures would plunge to −20°F and there would still be no snow. The ice would stay black and clear with pyramids of bubbles freezing into it like towering cumulus clouds. The bubbles made it easy to see how thick the ice was, and once it was three or four inches, it was safe for hockey. Our floppy brown rubber overshoes would mark the goals, we'd grab our hockey sticks, or just tree branches, and the game would begin…some kids in boots, some in hockey skates, Mum in old figure skates and my father in his speed skates. Dogs were always welcome to join the game, and a fire and hot dogs and a thermos of hot chocolate would be waiting on the shore. My mother was a pretty good skater, too, having learned to figure skate in Banff with the Simpson sisters who went on to skate internationally. I always thought it was magical to watch her and my dad circling the pond together, then start to waltz, striding in rhythm, arms across their bodies, left hand in left hand, right in right, cutting figures of threes and turns as they gracefully danced and spun around the frozen pond, my dad's long, silver speed skates flashing in the low sun, each stride sounding crisp and definite. As a finale, my dad would stride out alone, bent low and hands clasped behind his back, picking up speed, moving as smooth as maple syrup, then somehow he would twist, the long blades of his speed skates would glint in the setting sun, and there he would be, feet wide apart and arms gracefully held out from his side, leaning back as he carved a perfect arc in an elegant outside-edge spread eagle.

We still look for wild ice as the last skeins of geese fly against the leaden November skies of Edmonton. In good years we find it on the beaver ponds of Whitemud Creek and Elk Island Park , but now only rarely by Remembrance Day. The pure delight of skating on ice so clear you can see fish drifting below you is still there, but never again have I seen a couple waltzing against a backdrop of leafless willows and dark spruces, or an agile man on speed skates suddenly lean back in the pure grace of an outside-edge spread eagle.

BLEEDERS

JENNIFER QUIST

The place felt like a haunted mansion.

It was one of those old walk-up apartment buildings just off Whyte Avenue—the ones with great, grand names that don't make any sense like "The Centurion" or "The Blue Danube." Ours was called "The Apollo"—four storeys, dark red carpet in the hallways, velvet wallpaper in the foyers—the kind of cheap sumptuousness that hides decades of grime and grief. We lived there for four years, our kitchen window set where we could see the avenue through the gas bar of the car wash behind the building. We could see Whyte Avenue, lit up and reflecting off the black ice in the soapy alleyway, all winter long.

Even if we weren't so close to Whyte Avenue, our apartment building still would have been noisy every night, even in the winter. The floors creaked under feet we couldn't see—lonely students with illicit pet cats, lonely bartenders with illicit pet ferrets, Mormon missionaries, Chinese doctors who weren't allowed to practice medicine in Canada. Doors slammed closed, doors were propped open, letting the wind come moaning and freezing up the stairwells. Sometimes, someone would scream or cry loud enough for every one of us to hear. It made the earnest lady social worker who lived on the third floor crazy and she'd crank her Def Leppard CDs just to shut the rest of us out for a little while.

Most of the time, we were more ghosts to each other than we were neighbours. All of that disembodied human noise—it came through the walls, through the holes cut around the black radiator pipes that carried steam and water up from the basement boiler to heat our rooms.

The apartment building had a pair of resident managers. That was us. We were the people poor and desperate enough to agree to take responsibility for the rest of the tenants and whatever other poltergeists might smash out the glass in the back door or vomit half-chewed onion rings all over the second floor landing.

The building belonged to a retired plumber, our boss. All our rent paid for him to spend his winters somewhere far away—somewhere warm, somewhere nothing like the Apollo itself.

Like I said, the building was haunted by every one of us who lived there. And it wasn't just the noises that gave it away. There were the cold spots too. I don't mean the draughts from the single pane windows that sealed themselves shut from the inside with knobby veins of ice. There was another kind of cold in the building. Its corners harboured phantom zones of heavy, cold stillness—in the basement, the penthouses, it could be anywhere.

Our first winter as resident managers was a cold one—cold because before the landlord left for Aruba, he forgot to tell us about the bleeding.

"They need to be bled," he eventually told me, pushing aside my laundry basket and getting down on his knees on the carpet. He was prying back the metal guard over the heating pipes in the corner of our bedroom. "The pipes get full of air bubbles and the water won't flow. No water, no heat. So you need to bleed them."

I still didn't get it—not until I saw him stab and scrape at a radiator valve with the end of a flathead screwdriver. The building hissed out the long, cold breath it had been holding all winter. This was bleeding. Now, I knew.

When winter came again, I bled the radiator lines faithfully—maybe obsessively. I thought it was enough to keep us all warm. I thought it right up until the neighbour lady knocked on our door.

She was older than me but not old. I was twenty-one but I looked seventeen. And, however old she was, she looked like she was thirty. She didn't like that the building was abandoned all winter to punky managers like us—no one did. That night, she was standing in my doorway, trying to hand me a note. It was one month's written notice that she was leaving.

"We're going to have to move out," she said. "It's always freezing in our apartment and I can't take it anymore."

But I could fix it. I could show her.

She didn't care. When I remember her now, I see her standing in my doorway with her eyes closed. "Last night was unbearable," she said. "We found the warmest room and we all slept together—all three of us—trying to stay warm."

I couldn't stop explaining myself anyway. Her apartment was on the opposite side of the building from ours. The landlord must not have told me their heating line was separate from ours. No matter how compulsively I bled our pipes, theirs were still jamming with cold, empty space.

"Wait," I chirped. "Just let me bleed your lines. We just need to bleed them and everything will be fine."

I had the screwdriver. I was coming through the door, crossing the hall. I was heading for the bedroom where the lady and the two men who were her roommates had spent the night together shivering under a duvet, cursing the haunted mansion—and us.

I still don't know what these three people meant to each other. I knew their last names were different. But that didn't tell me anything about how they may have belonged to one another. There was nothing in the haunting of their rooms—no cries, no crashes, no creaks, no moans—that could tell me what had gone wrong there. Who had been touched, who had been left untouched—I'll never know. By the time I came through their door, I couldn't sense anything but the cold.

And it was cold in their apartment. The woman followed me inside, stood behind me, but wouldn't let me see her looking at me. When I twisted the screwdriver in the valve, the hiss the building let out was nearly strong enough to be a whistle.

"There," I said, grinning, satisfied. "It's all bled out. It'll definitely warm up in here before it's time to go to bed again."

But the lady was still extending her arm toward me, eyes closed, holding the written notice telling me she and the men couldn't stay here together anymore.

And there was no amount of bleeding that could have changed any of it.

CEPHEUS

JESSICA KLUTHE

Years of dust trembled through the air like the lightest snowflakes, each particle's path was illuminated by the bare bulbs that lined the walls of the church. Bits of hay stuck to the children's polyester robes and crunched under their feet as they shifted between Christmas carols. The nativity play was almost over. She slipped outside a few minutes early. At age seventy-three, she had a difficult time sitting in the hard pew. She wiped the sweat from her lip and wished she had sat in one of the pews along the side of the building where cool air slid in through the rough window frames. When the children shuffled across the stairs surrounding the altar and into position for their final song, she decided to slip outside a few minutes early. The heavy church doors shut behind her and shot out the warm puff of too many bodies belting out too many notes. Sophie still wasn't sure if it was her belief, or if it was her disbelief, that that made her feel so alive. Her face met the night. Her eyes, not yet adjusted, scanned the porch lights across the avenue. She felt the sting on her rough cheeks, the sudden sinking in the new snow, and the pulse in her fingers wrapped in worn leather gloves: this was her fifty-third Christmas Eve in Edmonton.

Sophie wasn't sure if it was some old ritual drummed up by the ooze of holiday around her, or if she had gone to church just for someplace to go. Her children and grandkids weren't arriving until just after lunch on Christmas Day. The highway had been too slick, her youngest son said, so he wouldn't be making it from Calgary until Christmas Day. Her other two sons had both flung themselves, at the first opportunity, to leave Edmonton for seasonless places. *Year-round summer, beach over lunch. What's not to love, ma?* Sophie understood their want to leave, even cursed the snow as her wrists and arms ached from scraping the sidewalks down to the cement, or from chipping the ice off the windshield even when she parked in the garage. But she never thought about leaving.

Inside, ritual played out: communion, peace-be-with-yous. Outside, ritual played out: the aurora's ghostly glow bent and fell. Sophie stood on the freshly salted cement steps of the church and wrapped her scarf around her neck and tucked the ends into her jacket. She watched as the rest of the congregation made their way outside.

A blonde-haired boy tugged his toque onto his head, and yelled "MOM! It snowed!" back into the church. His mom nodded while adjusting her son's hat and bending to slide his mitts over his hands. The boy smiled at Sophie and she pointed up.

"Cool!" he blurted and jumped down the steps and flung himself, a suited-up starfish, into a heap of snow. He turned over and tilted his head back to look up at the sky.

"Let's go. Into the warm car!" his mom ordered.

When the last car, with its trail of cloudy exhaust, pulled out of the rutted side lot, Sophie started to walk the few blocks home. The deep groan of the organ replayed in her mind. As she shuffled her feet over the icy patches and stepped firmly over the piles of snow, she saw the words, *"Ohhh come... ohh come... E-ma-a-a-nu-el. Bo-orn is the King of Is-ra-ellll,"* ribbon across the yards, fences, and snowed-over parked cars, and then wrap around her. The deep, drawn out –el, of Israel, would hold her for a second, slip around her, and then slide back between the houses. As bursts of wind ran through the trees, handfuls of snow fell from the branches that cradled them and then quivered to the ground. The wind skimmed over the rows of packed snow on either side of the sidewalk, twirled over the tops and twisted the loosened snow up toward Sophie's face. She whispered, *"Disperse the glo-o-omy clo-ooo-uds of niiigh-t."*

Before reaching her house, which would require her to walk on the road because there was a waist-high mound of snow on the sidewalk, she passed the collection site for the corner lot, a pile that would sometimes remain—even when brown, dry lawns emerged—into late May. She looked up. It was only at this time of year that in the most barren part of the northern sky, Cepheus—the constellation of the old hapless king—could be spotted. She squinted to see through the glow of the city's lights for his stars. When the sky was dark enough, she could trace the formation: it was a house-shaped constellation made of unstable, flickering Cepheid stars. She loosened her scarf so that she could tilt her head back. She could always locate the constellation by first finding Mu Cephei—the reddest star in the sky. She skipped her eyes over clusters of stars, and those in porch-light lines, until she found The Garnet Star. The rest of the constellation flashed into view. She watched Cepheus, whose stars rose and fell in a rhythm that she matched to her own breathing: a drawing in and an exhaling of crisp, winter air.

As she shook off her boots, she listened to the forecast. She'd left the TV on in the living room, intruder-prevention, she had thought before heading to the church. She watched as bubbly cartoon snowflakes twirled across the screen: "It will dip below thirty in Edmonton tonight, and we will be seeing flurries overnight until mid-morning. Christmas morning."

I WAS THERE

MARGARET ALMON

My parents moved from El Paso, Texas, to Edmonton in 1968, just in time for the coldest winter on record. I was a baby, but remnants of the story as told by my parents accumulated in my memory: My father being offered a job by the University of Alberta, over the phone (an American hired by a Canadian University sight unseen); my mother bursting into tears upon seeing downtown with the profusion of cranes, the city "bird"; the red Volkswagen Fastback without a heater, and blankets in the backseat.

My family's first Edmonton winter, 1969, and it was the one with the most days in a row below zero, January 7th – February 1st. Retroactively below zero Celsius, since at the time Canada was still using Fahrenheit. Until now, I told the story of it being the most days below minus 40, and that there were t-shirts for the survivors. In spite of being trained as a librarian, I had not researched this winter record, and I felt a temporary disorientation when I discovered only one day was 39 below, and the rest merely under minus 20.

I tell the 40 Below story as a way of introducing myself, now that I live in the United States again, moving back to the country of my birth in 1985. 40 Below is a magic number, where Fahrenheit and Celsius converge in a bi-thermal point of commonality, where my two homes meet, however briefly. In my memory, it is a triumph and a relief that the record stood, that minus 40 is minus 40, and maybe this is why I imagined a stretch of 26 consecutive days below 40.

The story rolls along to include ordering a car with air-conditioning, when none of the ones in Edmonton had it, because we drove to Texas in the summers. My crayons melted when I left them in the car one of the 4 days it took to go the 2000 miles. In Canada I was the American girl, who said "zee" instead of "zed" and ate my mother's tamales and enchiladas before Mexican chain restaurants moved up North.

Once back in the US, I was from Canada, and didn't comprehend pledging to a flag, and was baffled when my sister said she went to high school the first day it snowed and no one else was there, because it was a "Snow Day" and school was cancelled. I missed a US schooling in the American Revolution, and include my Grade 7 Social Studies class in my defining story, Canada: Evolution, Not Revolution. I didn't understand the dig in this title until I left Canada.

I wasn't born in Canada, and being in the US long enough, I lost my permanent resident status, which I suppose makes me an Impermanent Resident. I don't even have the certificate from the Edmonton Journal, illustrated with an igloo and declaring, "I was there. This certifies that I lived through Edmonton's record cold spell, Jan. 7th – Feb. 1st, 1969."

Recently, I found my Creative Writing notebook from Grade 5. The teacher asked us to write about why we like and dislike winter.

Tuesday November 29th, 1977

Why I like winter:
I like winter because you can go sledding and come home and have hot chocolate in a rocker by the heater. You can go skating and slip and slide in the snow.

Why I dislike winter:
I dislike winter because it's always cold and the snow makes an endless crunch scrunch sound. The dirty smell of the street snow. The cold whipping winds. And it gets dark so early. And when your mittens are wet and snow gets in your boots. You have to bundle up and it takes so much time to bundle up that you have to get up 15 minutes early.

My dislike of winter is more visceral at age 10 than my like of winter but it's missing the dramatic sense that has evolved in my storytelling. 40 Below is where I come from. I was there.

EIGHT DEATHS

MICHAEL HINGSTON

I've known eight people who died as a result of Edmonton winters.

In the '70s, one of the Phis got so drunk at our house Christmas party that he had to have his stomach pumped. The culprits were gin, a repurposed garden hose, and a high-ranking friend of mine whom I'd rather not name (he's a fellow millionaire now, with an excellent lawyer on retainer. I should know; I introduced them.). The downed Phi, though, was called Reed Phillips, and his leggy girlfriend ran in circles around his unconscious body, waving an alcohol-soaked candy cane and screaming, while we sat back in armchairs and counted the minutes until the paramedics showed up. He was carried off swiftly enough, but it was clear that the party was over. The pledges started to tidy up; it got so quiet you could hear the sirens as they pulled into the university hospital on what seemed like a never-ending loop. Twenty minutes after getting word that Reed was okay, I was having sex with his girlfriend in the house kitchen, her cheek down against the countertop, her arms flexed and quivering. My breath was very, very minty.

Reed, meanwhile, lay alone and goose bumped in the dark of the hospital. His bed was next to a window that for some reason had been propped open, and he was hooked up to clattering medical machinery that we were all about to find out was many years out of date. A few hours later, he choked on his own vomit and died (#1).

Then there was Alicia Lo, a friend of my sister's—she was taking a shortcut on one of those –40° mornings when a gust of wind suddenly blew through the back alleyway and knocked her to the ground. Her body wasn't found until two days later (she landed behind a dumpster, and we got nearly a foot of snow that weekend), but the coroner said she was completely intact: it was so cold that even the bugs wouldn't touch her (#2).

The High Level Bridge got Robin and Maxwell (#3, #4), old school-yard buddies of mine, three decades apart. I don't think they even really knew each other. Both jumped from heartbreak and what's now called SAD; both were dangerously under-medicated. And since the river never completely freezes over, it's possible that their bodies didn't smash into the ice on top. It's possible that, instead, they made it down into that sliver of exposed, steaming, rushing water. I never asked. And I try not to think about it.

Now, as you know, I worked out of our Calgary branch for many years, but because of this country's ridiculously optimistic understanding of distance, I ended up having to fly in and out of Edmonton a few times each month. I got to know that room in the Sutton Place like the back of my hand—even though at first they always tried to fob me off into some terrible corner of the place. You think ice machines are bad? Try a room next to the *gym*. And always near ground level. No, thank you. I need a view—if only to know it's out there. Open space, even just the idea of it, comforts me. There was this one clerk at the front desk who always took a little more convincing than the others, but I was able to make that smug piece of shit see the error of his ways soon enough. Last I saw him he was doing graveyard shifts for pool maintenance.

So eventually I got to know the whole staff. I tipped well. In return, they gave me a clear view of the entire city. One night I returned to the room after a late meeting over drinks, and, while shutting my curtains, I happened to look down to the pavement below me. It was dark, and the shapes were hard to make out, but my old street sense kicked in immediately: I was watching a mugging. A man with some kind of weapon was ordering an older woman onto the ground. He went through her purse, and looked as if he were throwing the unwanted items all around him. The woman, meanwhile, was on her knees and shaking her arms up and down in some kind of protest; it was the strangest thing. Keep in mind the streetlight directly above them was broken, so this was all happening in the shadows. I reflexively patted my shirt pocket, only to realize I'd left my glasses at the bar.

This continued for a couple of minutes, until suddenly the mugger looked up at the woman. His weapon, whatever it was, was held out in front of him, but gently, almost like a peace offering. I pressed my nose against the window to try and get a better look at what was going on. That's when I saw a flicker of movement underneath the next streetlight over—and then it was all over. The woman on the ground shrieked, the mugger turned, and the would-be hero slipped on a patch of ice and got either a bullet or a blade or a bottle through the stomach (#5). Who knows why people do the things they do?

One of my nephew's gay lovers had AIDS. It got bad quickly. Edmonton winter can turn a tickle in the back of your throat into organ failure (#6) overnight. I don't remember the kid's name, but there was definitely snow on the ground at the funeral. Some amateur groundskeeper cost me a pair of Oxfords that day. Was that much salt on the ground really necessary?

A communications SVP I was friendly with, and who in a pinch could be counted on to fill out a foursome on the links, was driving to work one morning when his car slid through an intersection and got T-boned by a garbage truck (#7).

Let's take a minute to reflect: when people talk about winter up here, they're not exaggerating. The cold is real. The wind is real. So is the ice. However, that does not excuse lazy or careless thinking. I'm not saying any of these people deserved to die. I wouldn't say that. That would be coarse. But when you leave too much up to chance, there's no telling what can happen, and if it was preventable, well, whose fault is that? That's all I want to say about it, really—that for the most part, what you call luck is an illusion. I didn't get to where I am today by crossing my fingers, let me assure you. A little pioneer spirit never hurt anyone. And that SVP? No winter tires.

Melissa Chong-Billings, my ex-wife, was killed off of Jasper Ave. a few years ago on Valentine's Day (#8). But I expect you already know all about that one, since it was in all the papers. So I won't get into it here.

I HEAR WINTER

RAYANNE DOUCET

There is a sound winter carries on the wind.
And it is deafening in the silence
of this frozen season.

There is a sound to frost as it brushes my fingers.
There is a sound to soil as it burrows
 in and succumbs to the snow that falls from above.
There is a sound to sun as it touches your skin.
Crisp, alert; ready for re-birth.

I hear winter hunch her shoulders
and curl into night.
I listen to trees as they groan
under the weight of the snow,
and sigh into the depth of winter.
I can hear Willows talk while
turning from young green teenager
to Grandfather in his rocking chair.
Leafless branches shaking gnarled fingers into the cold.

I hear human sounds.
Gortex jackets rubbing on Gortex ski pants.
Snowball battle cries.
Toboggan collisions.
Crunching boots on frigid ground.
Winter hearts beating loudly;
Taking cues from the converted Willows,
and two stepping with Old Man Winter.
I hear the ski hill roaring out his glory
in tune with snowboarders on his back.

I hear children building snow forts;
mini architects directing skyscrapers.

I hear parent's fingers squeaking on hot chocolate cups.

There is a sound as icicles form around the fog of our breath
There is a sound to air, tightening our skin
There is a sound to winter as it inhales.

BY ASSOCIATION

SAM LEAH

My father always said, "You learn by association." From my earliest memories, he would teach me and my sisters about associations before we even had a chance to know what the word association meant.

He was the only one to ever point out learning by association. Every parent teaches that way. Every child picks up on things that way. But Dad actually told you when he was teaching you by association. "It means two things go together," he would say. "Knives and forks, right? Thunder and lightning. When you fall, it'll hurt."

And then more customized Dad associations: "When I watch the news, everyone has to be quiet. Ok?" "When mom goes to the grocery store, you play quietly." "When we're in the car, we're quiet so Dad can concentrate, mmhmm?" "We're learning by association!"

Eventually Dad stopped saying it. My sisters and I were probably in our early teens when that happened. Not because he stopped teaching that way, but because he realized there was no need to be so heavy-handed about it.

The associations continued, though. And as we grew up, we made our own associations, about school (if I get really good grades, I'll go to university and I'll be successful), about fashion (when you wear blue, you don't wear black) and about relationships (if you're really interested in him, he won't be that interested in you).

But my favourite associations are with my city. I suspect I'm not alone in associating particularly momentous, or at least memorable events in my life with the river valley or with Whyte Ave or with the Yellowhead (believe it or not) or with Commonwealth or maybe even with the LRT.

But more than landmarks, my associations come with the seasons.

And of course I have spring, summer and fall memories, but Edmonton winters have always had the most impact on me. Yes, the winters are long and difficult, but it's the feeling created by the crispness and the claustrophobia of all that snow that made me feel closer to everything and everybody.

More importantly, though, all of those things seemed to provide me with a certain clarity that rain or sunshine or falling leaves never could.

For example, on a winter walk many years ago in the river valley: it was a quasi-first date. A rigorous trek through snowy, hilly trails, the terrain a built-in distraction for the possible lack of conversation and chemistry. We walked until we hit the midway point, a footbridge over the North Saskatchewan. The river looked beautiful, frozen and shadowed in fog. The date had been awkward and forced, a reflection of what many first dates lately had been. Later, I recognized it as the moment I refocused, decided to look for something better, something I was more worthy of. I associate that bridge with at least a little bit of growing up, making better decisions about the people I wanted to be around.

Another time, skating with a friend at Hawrelak Park. The day was average, −15, mostly cloudy. We walked out onto the ice clumsily and grabbed for the air in the first few minutes, but after some time, we became more fluid and brave with our movements, attempting mini-spins and almost falling. There was such a lightness to our moods, magnified by the beauty of the snow and the trees and activity that surrounded us. I got this feeling a lot, this invincibility that nature seemed to inject into a person for fleeting periods of time. But this one stayed with me. In the winter, when I drive up Groat Road, I go back to that feeling. I associate the park with a vow I silently took on that day of skating to be more grateful for everything I have. Sometimes it's the only thing that reminds me to give thanks.

And of course, there are those exceptional winters that you talk about for years and years until you start mixing them up with the other exceptional winters. There was that one, not long ago, my father asked for help. So much snow had fallen in the city that no matter which part of Edmonton you lived, it was a big problem and it was the only thing you could focus on. Dad needed someone to help him shovel off the roof. I think my mom's paranoia about "the roof caving in" had something to do with it, but she certainly wasn't going up. For almost a full day, we took turns going up onto the roof with a shovel or a snow rake or a spade (we alternated to make things interesting), pushing and sliding and lifting and throwing the endless snow off the house and into the yard. During one of my breaks, I went inside to make chocolate chip cookies. By the end of the day, we felt such a sense of accomplishment we were giddy with exhaustion. "I'm going to jump off the roof, Dad," I said. He looked at me with his most popular look: disapproval. "I'm doing it." He gave me the smallest smile. So I did it. I jumped off the roof and fell for no more than half a second before I hit the snow, that's how high it was piled. We laughed and then laughed even more when my mom started yelling from the house. From that day, I associate massive snowfalls with closeness, the closeness those storms bring to everyone in the city, but especially my family.

When it snows and snows and never seems to stop, I think about my dad. And when the temperature drops and drops and drops, I know that I love winter in the city. By association.

SANDWICH SEASON

MARGARET MACPHERSON

I'm the fourth of five kids, second girl, middle of the pack. It's a sorta nowhere place in a big family, easily lost in the mob. Dad calls it middle of the pack, a sister and two brothers on one side, another younger, cuter brother on the other. "Sandwich meat," he used to exclaim when we, the last three of his ragged, beloved children would stagger in from some wintery adventures. "Margie is sandwich meat between the bread brothers." My dad was big on the food metaphors.

And that's all well and good, except my mother didn't send meat sandwiches to school. Peanut butter with a dusting of wheat germ was more her style, or once, to my utter embarrassment, a beet sandwich. Imagine, leftover beets mashed between two soggy purple slices of bread. My brother got a macaroni sandwich once—mortifying yes, but analogous to how we, the youngest three, were united. After the first son (prime rib) and the first daughter (smoked salmon), a three-year gap ensued before Bill, David and myself presented in quick succession to become the inseparable starch siblings

We are each eleven months apart and with my mother's home barbering shear permanently set on "short" I dare say we even looked the same. Bill, Dave and Marg. Or, said really quickly, and slightly slurred: BillDaveandMark. It's the way I liked it. Three boys. Almost.

I didn't really have a gender identity crisis; I just didn't like being different from my brothers. The fact that I was different, that boys and girls react differently to different situations, came into clear and exacting focus one deep December afternoon with the temperature hovering in the mid-minus 30s. Why we would choose to go sledding on such a frosty day escapes me now, but decide we did, with Suicide Plunge the ultimate destination.

Now, this was no ordinary sledding hill. Suicide Plunge lives up to its name. It's a steep pitch that follows a narrow gully with a sharp turn halfway down and moguls—real honest-to-God moguls—at the bottom. It was a great hill but the slightest wrong move and you're tossed into the trees on the turn, or wiped out on the ice mounds below. There was also an unwritten rule that demanded sliders shout up to the top once they were clear, so the next foolhardy soul could take the daredevil plunge.

I didn't like the hill but I didn't dare say so.

My older brother Bill is the first to launch. With a running whoop Bill is down on his belly as his frost-fueled cardboard sled fires over the lip of the hill. Three or four minutes pass and we hear the all-clear signal from below. David looks at me. I look back. Yup, in birth order, it is clearly my turn, but bugger birth order, I'm not going. Not yet.

"I'll go last," I promise as my younger brother takes off. With a running thunk, he's gone, and then minutes later the sound I'm dreading. There is no question now. It is my turn. How long can I wait?

Well, turns out I could wait until both my brothers trudged to the top, all ruddy and partially thawed. "Go " they clamored. "Go." And then, as though I needed the ultimate insult, "Don't be a sissy girl."

Right. Down I go, belly to the snow pack, ice flying in my eye, I round the corner at top speed and rip down the final pitch. But I'd miscalculated direction, velocity, something, because I hit those bumps with such force, I flip up in the air, rotate twice and land smack on my back. The wind rushes from my lungs. I don't shout out because I can't. I try to inhale, I can't. I lie there, gasping for air. Is this what it feels like to be dead?

And that's when it hit, the thought that separates me from my brothers. What if I were dead? What would they do? How long would it take my brothers to come down the hill to check?

Ahhhh, attention seeking me! I lie silently at the bottom of Suicide Plunge convincing myself the hill had taken revenge, stolen my life. I lie there pretending to be dead as the cold creeps through my winter clothes and into my sorry body.

I hear a shout from the top, but because the dead can't speak, I don't. I simply wait for my brothers to come. They don't. In fact, unbeknownst to me, they decide it is, indeed, too cold for sledding. They pack up their cardboard and they go home.

Now, what's the point of pretending you're dead if there's no one around to witness your inert body? I want the shocked horror, the grief; I want sobbing strings in the background, violins and cellos, and my brothers' blanched faces surrounding my shimmering white coffin. I want them mute with blame and self-loathing. They'd goaded me, hadn't they? They made me do it.

Giving up and walking home now would negate the last ten freezing minutes and I realize, despite the cold, I will have to continue my charade until a search party is dispatched. Surely someone in my family will notice my absence?

The numbness creeps up my arms. I move my fingers in my mittens but somehow they have detached themselves from my hands. I wiggle my toes but are they mobile down there on the cold stumps of my dead feet?

A large black bird, a raven, flaps across my vision and alights in a nearby spruce. I am a corpse, food for the birds, but still I refuse to surrender my position. Where are my people? Don't they care? Tears of self-pity rise and pool, freezing on my chilled cheeks.

I imagine my mother, bereft, kissing me goodbye, but where is she? I am moved beyond moving by my own demise, paralyzed by pretending.

The minutes tick by. A second raven lands. Now I am beyond cold. I am bone chilled, numb. I realize if I don't move, I soon won't be able to, and then I really will be dead. It is this sobering thought and only this that stirs me. I stand, gather my forlorn self together and begrudgingly walk up the steep hill towards our home.

Inexplicably, my brothers are still outside, now playing road hockey with the neighborhood kids.

"Hey," they sing out in unison when they see me. "Marg, where you been? Wanna be on our team?"

And as I scramble to find my stick I realize that despite being as cold as I've ever been before in my entire life, I am now feeling much, much warmer.

I fire off a perfect slap shot, and like a reward for choosing ordinary life over high drama, my mother calls us in for gloriously gooey grilled cheese.

I THINK ALL DAY

MATT PRINS

It's quiet where I live. I live in the McCauley neighbourhood. It's a neighbourhood that most people would call dangerous. But it isn't. It's pretty quiet. It's especially quiet in the winter, but I guess everything's especially quiet when it's buried and muffled by snow. Everything's either dead or dormant. So it's not dangerous; it's quiet and buried. It's a nice atmosphere to get some thinking done. Even if I didn't want to, I naturally end up reflecting. I usually end up on Abbi. These beginning thoughts aren't about her, they're just of her. There she is. She fills the spaces in my mind and here I am being swamped with the feeling of her. With how if felt to listen to her, sitting next to her, her hand on the back of my neck. All these things of her consume me.

Under covers, when it's time to escape reality, she's there too. They're dreams but they feel a lot like nightmares. When I wake I feel my heart pounding and I have to stay awake and remind myself not to dream of her anymore. I say, "Don't fall back to sleep and continue that last thought of her," but sometimes I can't help it.

I spend most of the day alone. At the post office, I sort letters into the case—hundreds of letters. I just chuck 'em in there for a few hours. My mind turns off and my hands keep working and there's no way to distract myself. So again, the thought of Abbi creeps in. It surpasses thoughts of her and ventures into memories of things we used to do. And now I play out the present—what is she doing now?

Trudging through the snow. Bundled up in my parka and my mail-man's toque, sliding on slick stairways and clomping around and dragging my feet, I drop letters into mailboxes. Up and down the side-walks. Up and down, up and down, up and down, up and down. The quietness of suburbia becomes less so, when the thoughts begin their clamoring. We don't keep in touch. It was a bad end. She lives so far away, there's no hope of seeing her ever again. My fingers get colder and colder and when they get so cold that it hurts I snap out of those Abbi thoughts and now I can worry about whether or not I've done permanent damage to my flesh. Thank God.

At home I disrobe. I take a hot shower. I dress to stay inside. I put on a record and fill the sink. Do the dishes. Somehow, every night I have a pile of dishes to do and I put my cold hands in the warm water and I stand at the sink and I scrub and rub and place things on the drying rack. As the music warms the air I think about her. Was it the right thing? To split? I wonder if she's happier now or if she's miserable? I hope she's really miserable.

I have a nice living room and a big new TV and I watch movies from my couch. Movies help. Nice long ones are the best. Something really dramatic and romantic. I just watched Gone With the Wind for the first time and I didn't think about Abbi once in those three-plus hours. What a treat. Sometimes porn does the same trick. I connect my laptop to my big new TV and that's a good way to watch sex. Sex will make me stop thinking about her. I masturbate, my bare butt on my couch. My mind gets clouded with this nice filth, but sometimes it makes me wonder about the sex she's having. The type of sex. What if she's having this animalistic sex being steered by some disgusting sex maniac? Some dude with a six-pack and a huge wang? Sometimes her face slips into the shroud of porn lust and it makes me feel sick and I have to pull up my pants and turn the TV off. That's a day. We'll call it one day in a year.

I go to bed and it's quiet outside. We used to lie in bed on these kinds of winter nights. We'd just lay and warm each other and not say much. That was nice. Or was it? It had to have been. Am I glorifying the past? I wonder if she's thinking of nice things like this or only the bad. I think of more nice things and tell myself to stop it and then I think of the way it ended and I replay it all. Sometimes everything seems just. Sometimes it makes me real sad.

There's snow falling again. Just like last night. It makes it quiet and hushed and that's going to make me dream of Abbi. Winter is a good time to get some thinking done.

IF IT SNOWS

THOMAS TROFIMUK

Wake me if it snows. Always. If it is snowing and you are up and I am sleeping, wake me, please. Bring me back from sleep. Because when it snows, something is protected. Loneliness is evened out. Heartache is patted down. The patterns of life are quietly disrupted. And the world is made new.

Wake me if it snows. Always. Make tea. Or pour a scotch. Or open a bottle of wine. Pull up the comfortable chairs to the window and we will sit together in the dark and watch the snow fall. If you are cold, there is a soft and heavy blanket there in the blanket box. Or we can make a fire. Maybe we'll light a candle across the room—let its shadows dart and fret against the blue wall. We can sit together and talk about the skeleton of a jaguar they found in the Yukon, or the hazy image of a massive planet one hundred and seventy light years away, or the idea of morality without God. Maybe you'll tell me a story from when you were a girl. They didn't call it bullying back then. They didn't have a name for it. Maybe it was just cruelty. Maybe they used words like "hysterical" or lines like—"she's so sensitive." You might look up and nod and say: "nobody gets here without damage" and then you will carry on. You will be so nonchalant about this. It will neither diminish, nor underscore the damage. When you are finished your telling, I will love you again. I will be hopelessly in love with the woman who grew from that girl. To look into your eyes will be as if I am lost and found and suddenly angled in the world. It will frighten me a little to look there, but I will want to look because I will have rediscovered the gentle heart of you. And the whole while, it will be snowing. Maybe you will reach across the space between us—slip your hand into mine—and we will become silent, watch the snow as it dots the darkness. This soft brush that paints the night with white. We will not care what the time is. We will not mind getting up tired. You will sip your tea and smile. And still, the snow will be falling.

COYOTE

THOMAS TROFIMUK

Sandy brown, tawny fur streaked with black—
this coyote sideways steps on the packed snow.
She dances in her own sweet skinny-assed time
in front of my car. Eye on me. One eye always on me.
And I pull over. Stop.

"What are you doing?" my father says.
I do not point. That would be disrespectful.
"Coyote," I say.

You must be up from the river valley, I think.
But what are you doing here? (The river valley is
many blocks of houses away, and roads, and fences, and traffic.
And yet, here she is, in the middle of the city, a few hundred
feet from the house where I was young)

You think you hold nature back with your cities, Coyote says.
You think you're safe? You think I can't adapt to this?
Coyote smiles at me. She looks at my car with a careful,
ancient disdain. She looks at my car as if its heft and velocity
is irrelevant—its occupants insignificant specks of fluff.

"How do you know that was a coyote," my father asks.
"It looked and moved like a coyote," I say. I am curt.
My patience, after four hours of dinner theatre is thread-bare.
"You've seen them before," he adds, "in the mountains?"
He does not appear to need my confirmation.

She moves onto the sidewalk, into a front yard, around a pine tree
and then is gone—disappeared.

I am suddenly sad about this coyote.
But I know in my heart it is not the coyote.

It is my impatience with my father, who has been talking non-stop
for this 45 minute drive, about everything and anything—
like a three-year-old.
He has been filling space with words and I have been silently
blaming him
for being lonely. Like being lonely was his fault.
I help him into the house, hang up his coat for him, and say goodnight.
In the car, I sit for a long time as the past and the present
and the future swirl the night—they blur everything.
And then the coyote
trots by my car, across the boulevard and into the trees.

THE FATHER SHOVELS

THOMAS TROFIMUK

Shovelling the snow after work, I stop for a rest.
I place my hands atop the shovel handle and pause to catch my breath.
The sky is a mess of zinc and white and grey.
This snow has not stopped. It too, has only paused for a moment
to catch its breath. The snow is still falling, just not as hard as before.
Somewhere out back, tucked into the skinny cedars,
the sparrows sing.

I lean on my shovel and smile as I realize this is
exactly the same thing my father used to do, when he shovelled.
The same pause. The same half-lean on the shovel. The same gesture.
Except my father would have been smoking a cigar.
I remember watching him shovel from my bedroom window.
It seemed he would spend hours out there being meticulous with
the sidewalks and the driveway. Shovelling, and then sweeping.
Here's the thing. While the image of my father shovelling
and me watching
is crystal clear, I barely remember that kid. I don't know why he
was watching
from that window. I do not know what he expected to see except
this man
in the driveway in a futile battle with nature. The son was not
welcome there,
not yet. He was too young to be trusted with this important task.
There were distinct patterns to follow, things had to be done in a
particular way.
It was ritualistic and serious. It was a solemn duty.

Memory has a funny way of organizing itself. It can reform and new
truths emerge.
It's just that now, so many years later, with a young daughter in the
house as I shovel,

I realize my father never waved. He never acknowledged that I was there. I was invisible.

It was as if once he started to shovel, the contents of the house were irrelevant.

It's not that I wanted a connection. I don't know what I wanted. But this older self wishes

his father had stopped, and turned around, and looked up, and perhaps smiled.

That would have been something.

Just now, I look toward the house and scan the windows for her face. Because this

shovelling is not important—it is only something that must be done. And if I am

to be in this moment, I do not want to miss anything, or anyone.

BOYS OF WINTER

CLIFF THEROU

Partly, it was being a ten year old boy, but mostly, it was being a ten year old boy in Edmonton in 1963. It wasn't with any act of defiance or rebellion that we owned the streets and the playgrounds, it required no special bravery to walk across the schoolyard at any time, even into the darkness when the light descended early after school in winter. The soccer fields and playgrounds were ours to use as we wished. During recess we played an elementary form of soccer. Grey snow, packed hard from our constant running, as we chased after the school's frozen, plastic volleyball. No whistles and referees—our rules of the game had been passed down from the boys who had run there before and revised as we saw fit. Side streets in winter were our sidewalks as we walked three abreast to debate topics like whether a Shelby Cobra could take a 'Vette, or deep thoughts to speculate what would Wile. E Coyote do if he ever actually caught the Road Runner—never was the weather a worthy topic.

We played Saturday afternoon tennis-ball hockey on the street. Lumps of snow would mark our goal posts because a passing car, (always announced with the call "CAR!") could run over makeshift posts and they could be quickly and easily replaced.

This is a story of a time when parents did whatever parents did. They were simply the ones who told us to do our chores, shovel the walks, mow the lawns and come in for dinner when we were called. Parents would not be found at the side of our fields watching us—shudder to think that a boy might hear his name praised by a mother's voice in the presence of his friends; in 1963 it seemed some things were best kept in the privacy of one's home.

The ceiling of the Forest Heights skating rink was the winter sky. The puck-marked wooden boards surrounded the community, home to hockey for boys and figure skating for girls. Ron and Leo, my best friends, didn't play hockey and neither did I, but still we stuffed woolen socks into our skates and walked to the rink regularly with the laces tied together so we could carry the skates over our shoulders. I remember the straining street lights, stars and moon appearing as earnest and eager as our quick, often skipping steps to get to the rink. Certain evenings were designated for free, non-hockey skating. On these nights, we would skate under pale yellow lights to shrill, orchestral music which I will still only associate with skating.

These occasions were one of our early encounters with girls, as we would play tag or skate in lines, holding hands around the rink. These nights were sensual feasts; the sound of steel scraping on ice, frozen fingertips, and toes, gulping frigid air with laughing conversation and of course the warmth of holding a girl's mittened hand. To those boys who did not make the NHL, the magic of free-skate night became their loss.

INUIT SNOW

TRACY KOLENCHUK

When I was young, mom told me that Eskimos have dozens of words for snow.

Linguist Steven Pinker in his book 'The Language Instinct' claimed that, "Counting generously, experts can come up with about a dozen." Experts are wrong, I learned when I visited the frozen north.

It's a shame, growing up in Alberta that we have so much winter, but not enough words to describe it. Maybe we need to learn to speak Inuit to learn all the words for *aniu* (snow).

The first winter I remember was in grade one, I was five years old. A *piqsiq*—a blizzard; it snowed and snowed and snowed and snowed. Cold blowing snow—*natiruvaaq*—that drifted so high it covered cars and *qimaugruk*—snowed-in some elderly residents.

In recess, we cut snow-blocks—*Auviq*—with our hands and created our own igloo snow-forts, as we struggled through the *Mauja*—deep soft snow—to carry them back to the base. We had no *tagluk*—snowshoes.

We had to avoid the *Katakaqtanaq*—crusty snow that breaks when you walk on it because it doesn't have the strength to make walls.

And *Qaliriiktaq*—crappy snow that is no use at all, like *Qannialaaq*, soft, fluffy snow—what the skiers call 'powder'.

And *Kiniqtaq*—damp snow, because, although it is perfect for snow-balls, it doesn't hold together well enough to carry the bricks to our fort. We didn't need mortar—this wasn't built to last.

The best snow for snow-forts and igloos is *Natiruvingniq*—hard packed, drifted snow that can be cut into solid blocks, hopefully not too heavy for a five-year-old to carry but strong enough to build a fort.

Morning recess was short, but we continued our work through the lunch hour, eating wet sandwiches as the *Masak*—wet snow, stuck to our mittens.

Once we had our fort built—we only needed three walls—facing the opposing warriors, we started to create *Sinuupa*—snowballs, to prepare for war.

We had an informal Geneva Convention with regards to the arms.

No *Sikuliatlait*, ice crystals in the snowballs. No *qiqsruqaq*—snow glazed by thawing and refreezing. No *sitxiq*—hard crusty snow.

In afternoon classes, we all watched the *qannik*—snowflakes, outside the windows, anticipating the coming battle.

By afternoon recess, the forts were ready, well-armed with snowballs.

The *Qannizniq*—snowfall, had apigaa snow-covered everything with a new smooth layer.

And the *Natiruvaaq*—drifting snow, had filled in the cracks and actually created a hard *Qimugjuk*—snow bank on one side, a natural entrance.

The afternoon had warmed a bit, and the *Aquillutaq*—fresh new snow was *auksajaq*—melting snow, perfect for snowballs.

The battle began!

In a few minutes, we'd completely used up our stored weapons and both impromptu teams were running to the *Qimugjuk*—the nearby snow banks—for more arms.

Soon we resorted to destroying each other's forts, causing *sisuuq*—snow slides or avalanches, burying our opponents, and ourselves, for a few seconds.

Illuktuq—snow blinded, we had to *puuvruktuq*—plow through the snow with our bodies to escape.

Then the recess bell rang. Back to class.

This was in 1957.

It wasn't long before the school principal called all of the ringleaders (I was supposedly one of them) to the office.

We were not allowed to make snow forts, snowballs, to have snowball fights, to destroy snow-forts. No pushing, no shoving, no fighting.

We were all, about 18 of us, getting the strap.

We lined up, and, the principal took a few deep breaths. He knew he needed to pace himself.

It didn't really hurt. Our hands were already *qaubrimaitchuq*—numbed from the snow. He stopped as soon as they turned red, which for most was on the first or second stroke. We tried not to laugh, and not to skip, as we walked solemnly back to class.

The school day ended, we enjoyed the *qanniksuq*—light snowfall, no wind—all the way home.

We didn't tell our moms.

METAPHOR FOR WINTER

ANN SUTHERLAND

My 14-year-old son zips up his winter jacket, stuffs his feet into his sneakers, and heaves his knapsack onto his back. His hockey helmet is securely attached to the outside of his pack. He grabs his hockey stick, his skates slung over it. He's ready for the four-block walk to his junior high school. His plan is to stay after school for a game of shinny at the community rink.

He thinks he's ready. I know better.

"It's minus 20 with the wind chill. Don't forget your mitts. What about boots? You need a toque on. Exposed flesh will freeze in 10 seconds." I cringe at my own nagging voice. But he is my son, and I couldn't live with myself if Old Man Winter caught him in his icy grip.

My son doesn't answer. His eyes roll and he shoots a look of annoyance my way. He holds up his hands to show me he's wearing his hockey gloves. He clumsily opens the back door and cold air rushes in like hockey players charging onto the ice.

"There's a toque in your knapsack if your ears get cold," I shout as he slams the door behind him. I am smug with having got the last word in and with my cleverness for sneaking winter armor into his pack.

Ten seconds later the door opens and a black toque flies into the house.

My son is asserting his independence. Winter seems to be the best season for him to do this. He ignores his toques and mitts, and he prefers sneakers to heavy-duty Sorels. If the temperature is hovering around 0°, he'll wear shorts. He thinks he's invincible. And he is. He simply ignores the bone-chilling air. It's beyond me how he doesn't lose an ear or nose to frostbite.

I watch out the window as my son comes alive outside in the cold, bouncing along down the sidewalk to school.

I grab my coffee and sit down at my computer to write about winter in Edmonton. My thoughts drift to my son, and I realize the metaphor for winter is all wrong. Winter is not an old man, slow and arthritic. Winter is a hormonal temperamental teen roaring toward adulthood. It's intense in its energetic youthfulness. It's full of frosty vigor, one day bringing with it light and giddy snowflakes. Its mood changes the next day as sulking grey clouds settle over this flat city. And as you breathe in air that will surely freeze your lungs, you try to figure out this season and its diamond-filled snow that vexes and mystifies and beautifies.

It begs you to come play. We shuck off caution and bullet recklessly down toboggan hills. Snow Valley crawls with skiers like ants up and down the hill. The pond at Hawrelak Park, dormant in the summer except for geese and paddleboats, comes alive with skaters.

The next day the moody teen that is winter pushes you away with a bone-chilling cold and a dump of snow. We butt heads and fight it with our winter war machines. Yellow graders lumber along Jasper Avenue. Growling snow blowers and jiffy bobcats shift snow from one side to another. And in the wee hours of the morning, snowplows prowl down back alleys as if on a reconnaissance mission.

In the end, we can say we survived. It's a miracle really, that Edmonton can breathe under the weight of snow and cold. We can brag about statistics and quote newspaper headlines: 'Only Dzalinda, Siberia colder. Edmonton bottoms out at −46, −58 with the windchill.' It's something to hang onto, something to be proud of, like your child coming in second in the citywide school essay competition.

By noon, the air has warmed to −13. I need a break to clear my mind. I pop in my contact lenses (glasses fog up at anything below −8), layer myself in my running gear and head out. That first intake of cold air catches me by surprise. I remind myself I've run in colder weather. I head toward my familiar running route along the North Saskatche-wan. I ease into a rhythm and channel the teen psyche of embracing and defying. Perhaps it's the only way to survive an Edmonton winter.

It seems to work. The cold fades as my body heats up.

I forget it's −13 and instead embrace my surroundings. The sky is a brittle blue and the thin winter sun hangs low. The North Saskatchewan River, high-banked and carved deep, is laid bare. It's this black and white landscape that reveals the bones of an ancient valley, stories of a geological past, undiscovered dinosaur bones, first nation settlements, explorers, fur traders, and immigrants.

Everywhere there is a story, from the curious coyote up ahead, to the distinct maniacal yucka-yucka-yucka of the Pileated Woodpecker somewhere in a nearby tree. Near the Hawrelak Park foot bridge, I pass a small spruce tree decorated with ornaments. It, too, has a story. I was told that dog walkers decorate it each year at Christmas as a tribute to their dearly departed pets. I don't know if this is true, but it's a good story just the same, imagining that each decoration holds the story of a beloved pet.

Back home, it's 3:30 and the temperature has actually risen to −10. The light angles low, and muted colours emerge. Grey, pink, purple, yellow, blue. You need to look closely to see what a complicated and beautiful thing winter is. Right now, my son will be heading to the rink with his friends and lacing up his skates. In their minds they rival any NHL player. In winter, anything is possible.

My son returns home in the 5:30 darkness. His ears and cheeks are rosy, his eyes bright. He's chatty, describing in detail the goal he scored and how his friend Jeff said it was just like the one Gretzky made once a hundred years ago when the Oilers won the Cup. "I practiced that move a million times," he says.

I move in close to him without invading his personal space. I can feel the cold hovering around him. As he chats away, I take a deep breath. He smells like winter—fresh and alive with the promise of adulthood waiting beneath. His story waits to emerge.

BEGINNING THE END

JOAN SHILLINGTON

Eighty-seven years old. It was as if my mother was a young woman again canning peaches and putting up blackberry jam just like the autumn I was six and she gave me the job of chopping the tops off carrots.

My left pointer finger…slips beneath the knife
and she settles me on the back step,
blood soaking through the tightly bound facecloth,
weeping red drops on the concrete,
mother determined we wait the hours
for Dad to come home and take me
to the Royal Alexandra Hospital.

I turn away as the doctor freezes and stitches
hanging skin. Dad's whiskey breath louder
than antiseptic.

But all that fall she played Euchre with the Seba Beach Seniors, bringing a serve-twenty pasta casserole each week for pot luck. A bad chest cold kept her home New Year's and by January 23rd, pain gripping her lungs, an ambulance rushed her to emergency. Exhausted and on the restless edge of medicated sleep, she was sent home. Flaming shadows awakened her. A fire in the garage! Its fingers licking the interior. Billowing smoke into −40 air, scourging the air

just as my cries did years ago
when the anesthetic lost it's grip on my finger.
Pain clawing up my arm.

Now, fifty years later, she rises. Coughing pnemonia, trailing the steel cylinder of her next breath and dials 911 for the second time that night.

WINTER PERSPECTIVE

MATT INGLIS

What can be said about winter in Edmonton? It's cold, it's windy, there's a lot of snow, and traffic is awful. It's all true. This city is filled with negative perceptions of winter. Up until a week ago I was part of the majority of Edmontonians who hated winter and everything about it. The weather never changed, the traffic still sucks, and there's still more snow than I want to look at.

So what did change? I used winter as a last-minute final project, and it worked. I'm a television student at NAIT, and one of my final assignments was to put together a three-minute news feature. Seems easy enough: three minutes of video and a story to go with it. It was assigned in early fall, giving me more than enough time to put together a good story. That wasn't exactly the case. I went in search of an emotional, hard-hitting story. I had no luck with that, running into roadblocks everywhere. Cancelled interviews, bad weather preventing travel, etc. When the day came to hand the assignment in, I still had nothing. I racked my brain for any hint of a story that could give me a passing mark, when it hit me. I'm a Canadian. What is the biggest issue Edmonton faces every year? The weather.

So after warming up my car, I hit the streets. The idea was simple: Put together a story on winter in Edmonton. I figured if I was lucky I'd get one person with a positive opinion on winter, to give my story balance. So off I went, first to get some footage of the city itself. I stopped on Saskatchewan Drive, put on my coat, threw on a scarf and grabbed my gloves before setting off to get a perfect image of Edmonton in winter. Perfect is what I got. I made it to my ideal location, set up my tripod, and looked through my viewfinder, and to my surprise, I didn't see a cold, desolate arctic tundra like I'd always pictured. I saw a city glistening with crystals, sun bouncing off the fluffy, white snow and illuminating the river valley. I stayed for a few minutes, sitting on a park bench, admiring the city from my vantage point. Reality set back in and I realized I still had work to do.

I got to Whyte Ave expecting to find a dead city street where I could film empty sidewalks, showcasing how winter hurts business in Edmonton. Yet again, to my surprise, Edmonton was alive. People just like me, bundled up in their scarves and mittens, were going about their day as if it were an August afternoon. So I stopped in at a local watersports shop. There's no way watersports shops can stay afloat on ice, right? Wrong. This particular shop has adapted to winter, specializing in tropical travel, snorkeling, and scuba diving. Well, there's the positive side to my story, now to find a negative side. It was a particularly chilly weekday, so I figured a local ski hill would be a good place to show the negative effects of winter. People don't ski in minus twenty, right? Wrong again. I was on a roll here. The cold is awesome for business at the local hills. Since they make their own snow, when it's a cold year they can start making snow early, and finish early, resulting in a longer season. And the cold doesn't slow down the snow sport enthusiasts: The hill was full of skiers and snowboarders taking advantage of the mix of natural and manmade powder. I was starting to see a trend here. Maybe I'm the Grinch and winter isn't all that bad.

I needed to know the science behind winter here in Edmonton, so I headed to talk to a local meteorologist. On my way across the city, I saw a man jogging. In minus twenty, he was outside, by choice, running. I had to talk to him. So I swung into a parking spot and approach this man running sets of stairs by the High Level Bridge. "Uh, what are you doing?" I ask him. "This is my way of attacking Edmonton winters!" he exclaims. "I'm an Edmonton baby, born and raised. I learned that winter isn't going away. You just have to learn to deal with it. Dress for the weather and get outside."

This single, cheery Edmontonian was what I needed. I had a new perspective on this city during winter. But I had a project to do, so I went to meet the meteorologist. He tells me, in more scientific terms, Edmonton isn't all that cold. We have trends, cold snaps and warm fronts. But they're just trends. Edmontonians have this false idea that we have it so bad. Considering how far north we are, we've got a pretty tame winter.

Alright, so this guy is a scientist, of sorts—a professional, if nothing else. He says it's not that cold, but I've experienced it. It gets pretty chilly. But I got something out of what he told me. It's all about perspective: from the shop manager who adjusts for each season, to the ski hill owner who prays for long, cold winters, to the jogger who runs to fight Mother Nature on her own turf, to the meteorologist who sees the reason behind it all, to the young reporter who has an epiphany.

So I finished the story and actually learned something from my day experiencing the different angles. Winter is what you make of it. Unless you plan on making a run south of the border, you're stuck with it. So embrace it and appreciate the summer when it comes. After all, we wouldn't be Canadian if we didn't have winter.

IN THIS TOO A STRANGE BEAUTY

ANNA MIODUCHOWSKA

Whitemud Drive dozes across the Groat Road bridge.
In a recurring dream

water streams into its bed, cars sprout fins,
the flow of traffic miraculously attuned to the current.

Mallards slice the surface with the backs of their feet—
a first-rate thrill that leaves no scars. They come

to a full stop in the shade of an aspen
serenely copulating with the wind, begin to feed.

But it's February, winter sun about to die
in a band of cloud eager to deliver

the bitter weight it has ferried across the Rockies.
A snow plow shrieks by—its blade

would do Hephaistos proud—flurry of sparks,
the surface scraped so it hurts to look.

Headlights scurry in pairs more or less
aligned, the ears inside each vehicle

plugged into singular frequencies,
each heart a brazen anvil.

A WINTER LESSON

ALAN SCHIETZSCH

A shoe softly drops onto the cool hardwood at my feet, rolling to rest against the side of my socked foot. I glance up from my weekend Journal, puzzled.

Emily, my toddler daughter, is already wobbling unsteadily away.

Ah, she's given me a 'present,' I realize, charmed at her play. Back to the escape of my paper.

Plop! The other shoe drops. And it is the other shoe, too. "How about that", I marvel, "a matched pair." Emily has figured out which of her two shoes belong together.

I look down and smile.

But Emily has already turned away, having completed her gift. So I turn back to my reading.

I snap back to attention: Plop. This time it's louder. My boot. And she's gone again.

Is she going to relocate the entire shoe rack?

Plop! It's my other boot. I guess so.

Whoosh-shuff-click.

OK, that sounds odd—zippers and snaps clattering as my ski jacket has been dragged across the floor and deposited in front of me. Now she has my full attention.

Before long, mittens appear, and a snowsuit, and—no words—Emily has told me it's time to drop the paper and take her outside. It couldn't be clearer.

The proudest dad in the world, who am I to say no?

She's figured out exactly what's needed. Not just for herself, but for me too. Before she can even talk.

Not the shoes, although they are important. Not the clothes, or the mittens.

What's needed is to engage. To go out. To spend the day together. To enjoy the snowy mounds beside the sidewalk, to see each other's smiles, warm in Edmonton's winter air.

I went on to lose my dread of winter. Emily went on to become a ski instructor.

Lesson learned.

OH, EDMONTON

DIANA S. ADAMS

Ice crunch of tires scares
magpies to the tops of trees
her hat's knit like a cake
his, a small animal
that could have survived winter
It's too cold for conversation
stored words
keep them warm.

EVENING ALL AFTERNOON

DIANA S. ADAMS

Spurious gasps
over multiple pots

chain me
to a dining room chair

colours of the dog
& floor combine

ice cracks the spine of the house
& the only thing growing is snow

I calculate what it will take
to get Spring

to my plate. My mind
rotates its bits of loathing

AGORAPHOBIC

DOLLY DENNIS

A day without   colour
     Snow shavings weigh the lilac tree.
Sparrows' nest in desiccated twigs
     Sits between bisected branches   now lays bare.
And, oh, the mouldy sky sulks in winter's light
     Sighs and sieves its granular coat.
Veils of hoar crochet the shrubs
     Where mice now sleep in lullabies of three.
Come out to play   the abandoned crow shrieks
     Come out to play.
In the beam of street lights overhead   stud diamond earrings
     pierce the snow   await my steps.
A slivered opening and I am out—
     Feel the rush   a cataract wind blinds my path.
I covet the sleep of mice   now frozen in the undertow of ice.
     I seize the door and lunge inside
Shut the universe and its storms—
     Spring
         Perhaps
           I may try again

COLD COMFORTS

DON PERKINS

Winter's onset, no real test;
First snow, chilling outs the child within
to new first snowballs
and the always surprise of
softening sounds and horizons

Winter's never-end,
testy time
warms too slowly
eternally adolescent
impatient, foolhardy,
single-minded
gotta get outta here
time of year

Midwinter, Rossetti's bleak mid-
Winter—when snow keeps falling
snow on snow and icy winds make moan—
a multiple choice exam:
takes our most mature measure,
calls us out, bids us name,
calibrate and celebrate
the many modes of
cold:

Wet, dry, deep, bone-chilling,
can't feel my feet, face;
hands and toes gone numb, death
-dealing brass monkey
freeze your nuts nose ears and tits off,
buck up you're a Canadian
just learn to live with it
cold;

square-tired, arctic, oil-pan cracking,
turn metal so brittle it snaps from this
cold;

can see all the way to the edge of the universe
the sky is so clear tonight
cold;

Hear the northern lights snap and crackle
from over the horizon
cold;

too frigid for wolverines
why can't we hibernate
with the bears anyway
cold;

too bad we don't have a fireplace,
where's the extra blanket bed sox
fleece pj's and thermal nightie too
cold for sex
cold.

Scorn that last—
hold out, embrace
that flesh-to-fleshly
rub two willing bodies together,
generate some erotic heat kind of
cold;

that fill the maternity wards,
keep the midwives hopping
late next September
creative kind of
cold—

O JACKIE

B. JOANNE UNDERWOOD

your memory's as bright
as the clear blue sky
that November winter day
when you were seventeen
sunlight glinting   off crusty piled-up snow
temperature deep in the minus range
in downtown Edmonton   and when
you see pedestrian exhaling mushroom cloud
of breath   over his dull black parka
with the fur-trimmed hood
see those big Sorel boots trudging along
and those lips mouthing words
asking if you've heard
then giving you the news

it seems so strange
so other-worldly
compared to the scene
on six o'clock news
of a pink pillbox hat
in a black Lincoln convertible
on that very same blue sky day
only her day was in Texas
and her husband had just been shot
then your mind embraces your
Canadian cold   Canadian snow
and for you
winter in Edmonton leaves nothing
nothing at all to complain about

A SHORT THANK YOU NOTE TO SEAMUS HEANEY

STUART THOMSON

To the bedroom window the sound travelled up from the driveway: a harsh rasp followed by a soft thud. It repeated monotonously. I pulled the curtains to see the old man, quick as a piston, stabbing the shovel into the ice-crusted snow and lifting a clump of it onto the growing banks that hemmed him in. He didn't take breaks, not even a pause after he lifted the snow and dumped it beside him.

It looked like a cold one. His breath erupted through the balaclava as he brought the shovel down. It hung there and he brought his head back through it on the way up.

The white snow shone incandescent against the uncovered black-top of the driveway. It was his first year of shovelling snow like this. My dad would have the whole thing done in half the time it took the neighbours, punching furiously at the snow until it slumped along the snowbanks and cursing the flakes that continued to fall. Cursing Canada, cursing Edmonton and jokingly longing for the cold, miserable drizzle of Aberdeen.

I felt a cold pang of guilt as I dressed, pulling on long johns and a soft fleece sweater. I wrapped a scarf around my neck and put my coat on. I hunted for my gloves, which were drying on the heating vent after last night's shovelling. My toque, still damp, was on the floor. I laced up my battered Doc Martens and touched lightly the pockets of my jeans before pulling the door open.

The fat flakes hung in the air, suspended. Against the iron winter sky they looked like ten thousand stars.

"Too late," he said, half joking. "There'll be more soon though." He pointed up at the falling snow.

I felt the cool wind of reproach.

"I think I'll go for a walk. Since I'm all bundled up," I said.

He nodded.

The house diminished with distance and I felt the truth of the cold as I walked. It was the kind of cold that startles the soft flesh of your legs and makes the inside of your nose crackle and sting. They had said on the news that exposed skin would freeze in 30 minutes in this weather.

There's something clear and crisp about the world in these conditions. For a short while, the brain sheds any unnecessary thoughts and focuses, laser-like.

-The frigid beauty stands in contrast, plumed against a white canvas. Everything breathes. The sombre pines stand solemn against the emerging pink of the afternoon. The bright radiance of winter lends itself to beauty. Light is everywhere, bouncing back and forth in a reflective dome. Suffer the cold to see it because nothing comes free.

The park was deserted and I took a path through a wooded area to shelter from the wind. The trees leaned above me. The soft, thin layer of snow covered the ice that grumbled underfoot.

-Why are the pines sombre and solemn? That's just how they look. And that's how I feel looking at them. Beauty is more than just how something looks and the stark contrast of its radiant harmony. It's all the feelings. The swelling of the cold air in my chest.

The pines' tiny leaves held fast in the wind and the branches recoiled as if stabbing back at it. The pines were one of a few things familiar to me.

-Art is to communicate those things, and help people to imagine it. You could write a song about the swelling of the cold air in my chest.

You could paint an accurate picture of the trees and it wouldn't tell anyone about the swelling of the cold air in my chest when I see the dark, solemn pines. Art isn't about beauty, but beauty is still important.

The wind whipped my face.

-Art could simply be about communication. One man imparts something to another.

-Someone said: the task of words is to make you hear and feel. A task of unremitting failure. How to even start?

The cold slows everything down: half-formed words and vague utterances flooded my mind. Fifteen minutes is about enough. Fifteen minutes, halfway point to frozen flesh.

I had wandered down a path in the park, it had forked and turned, and I was unsure which direction was home. Lost in my thoughts, I'd walked without worry about where I was going or where I'd been. Through the pine trees there was a red light in the distance, like a fading coal in a fire. It could be the tiny neighbourhood, or it could be some distant street light, or it could be a cruel apparition created by a glaciered brain.

It was silly, to go for a walk and get lost in the park. Just a silly thing that gets serious in the fierce wind and winding path that could lead anywhere.

Panic and humiliation sat faintly in my stomach, threatening to replace the discomfort of the cold.

I traced my way back to the fork and looked down both paths. The wind had scratched out my footprints. Maybe a wrong decision could mean frostbite, skin blackened and seared. How long did it take to die in the cold? If skin freezes in 30 minutes, the rest of you can't be far behind.

My scarf slipped down and my freezing cheeks caught fire. My fingers were painfully numb and I tried to savour the pain. It's not frostbite if it's sore, but you better start worrying when you don't feel anything. I still felt something.

I took the path that seemed to go in the direction of the red light and I trudged quickly. The path turned and I lost sight of the glowing apparition. The wind howled between the trees. I couldn't think a whole sentence. My brain had latched onto a line from a poem: "streets that follow like a tedious argument."

-Trails that follow like a tedious argument. Streets that follow. Sawdust restaurants. There's a Jack London story where a man dies in the cold. The dog survives. The man dies because he falls in water. Freezes. Beats his hand against his chest to get some feeling. Tries to light a fire. Fails. Communicates the cold. Feel it in your feet.

The trail turned again and opened up into the park and the entrance was a hundred feet away. I looked at my watch: thirty minutes. Five minutes to get home.

-Should be OK. The man was embarrassed too. About to die and embarrassed about it. His instincts failed him. Or he failed his instincts.

The street lights were on to combat winter's early gloam. The pale light blurred into the dull sky. I couldn't find the red light I'd seen from the path but I could still see some version of it in my mind.

The house grew in front of me.

The bedroom light was still on and the desk was illuminated above the driveway where a thin layer of snow was building. A fierce flame warmed the inside of my chest. There was work to do.

CUTOUTS

ERIKA LUCKERT

This year for Christmas, I'm picking up the pile of old drafts and rejected printouts of poems full of typos and clichés and I'm taking each sheet and folding it in half so that I can see the words crossing over each other, faint through the page, and I'm folding them in half again and again, until I pick up the scissors and carve my old words into snowflakes.

When I unfold the first, I try to read the words that I haven't cut away, but I can't remember the letters that fit between the papery arms of the snowflake I've made, so I cut out another, and then another, until my floor is covered with snipped-away clichés and my desk is covered with word-flakes.

I pin the cut-outs to my window and look through them to see that there's still no snow on the ground outside, and so I try to cut star-flakes out of the sky, my eyes snipping triangles, wishing I knew how a snowflake is made, or how a poem falls.

THE GIRL IN THE SNOWSHOES

NICOLE MOELLER

"Auntie?"
There is a five-year-old tugging on the sleeve of my winter jacket. I dare not make eye contact.

"Auntie!"

She won't let up.

Despite the fact that I bought her a hot chocolate, lay in the freezing snow to make her a snow angel, (not easy when you're five months pregnant), engaged her in lengthy discussions on the different variations of yellow coloured snow, and gracefully ignored the snot dripping down her nose, she still won't let up.

"Let's go!"

She is insisting that I do the thing I'm not capable of doing:

Cross the parking lot.

At certain times of the year—like, for example, today—crossing this parking lot is a death wish. Why? Because it's turned into a sheer sheet of ice. Why? Because of yesterday.

Yesterday.

When everything warmed up; when everything melted.
Don't get me wrong. I love when it warms up. I get an extra spring in my step. Hope, I think it's called. Suddenly I feel...

Lighter.
Thinner.

Gorgeous.

Hell, I *am* gorgeous.
I take off my toque and let my hair flow. My mind wanders to the summer and how great it's going to be. How *different* it's going to be. How different I'm going to be. I imagine myself… biking.
Biking for three days through the river valley. And when I'm not biking, I'll be hiking. And when I'm not hiking, I'll be running up those stairs. You know the ones.
By the Glenora Club.
The ones people run up and down…*for fun*. Well, that's going to be me. Because this summer is going to be different.
That's what I thought.
Yesterday.

But today is today. Today the temperature has dipped to approximately minus seven thousand and summer is a distant memory. The words biking, hiking and Glenora stairs are enough to throw me into a homicidal rage. Today my skin is dry, a bright red rash has taken over my entire body, and this parking lot, the one I could have skipped through twenty-four hours ago, has turned into a giant skating rink.

I don't do skating rinks.

Which is unfortunate, because on the other side of this parking lot, down the path, through the trees and into the clearing, is the most amazing view of my city.

Edmonton.

There's a certain spot I stand in where I can see the river curve around the bend, the High Level Bridge in the distance and Hotel Macdonald in front of me. I can't hear the cars. I can't hear the people. I can't hear anything. It's the beauty of the city interspersed with the silence of the country. A silence that exists only in winter. A silence that is so deafening it makes me feel…
at peace.

Calm.
It makes my body do something I didn't think was possible anymore.
Relax.
My shoulders pry themselves away from my ears... my breathing slows down… my thoughts stop.
Finally.

And I just…enjoy the view.

It's my favourite spot in the whole city. My favourite moment of the whole year. A moment only possible in winter.

Now, if only I could get there.

I've often thought of starting a support group. Edmontonians Afraid of Winter. Or Edmontonians Afraid of the Ever-Present, Unexpected, Underlying Danger that Winter in our Beautiful Northern City Inevitably Brings. Anonymous.

But since everyone in the support group would be afraid to leave their house, it wouldn't be much of a support group. So instead, I spend four to six months of the year hiding out in my Alberta Avenue home. Alone.

Sort-of. My cat Charlie is holed up with me, of course. And yes, from time to time he sits by the door and begs (in the form of shrill, never-ending meows) to be let out. A request which is always denied.

It's winter, Charlie. Anything could happen.

Winter in Edmonton: Anything can happen and everything does. Perhaps that should be our city's new slogan. A hidden patch of ice, a highway closure when you're trying to get home, mistletoe…you never know what you're going to get.

I've always been this way. Afraid of winter and all it entails:

Ice.
Snow.

Santa Claus.
The Olympics.
All of it horrifying.

Rather than trying to join the troopers who embrace this season, I have always dropped out, turned and ran, fallen over.

Yes, you heard me correctly. Fallen over.

I was the kid in seventh grade who, while cross-country skiing with my classmates, suddenly, purposefully, without any hint of grace, fell over.

Sideways.
Into the snow.
As if I'd suddenly had a massive heart attack.

Our lesson in cross-country skiing had turned into downhill skiing, as my classmates started to race down a "giant" hill outside of our school. I panicked and instead of attempting the hill, I fell over, faked an ankle injury and performed a terrible limp all the way back to school. And over the next few weeks, every time my class went skiing, I went snowshoeing.

That's right.
I'm that kid.

The one who provides a written argument to the teacher on the benefits of snowshoeing. The one who claims that it's undemocratic to be forced to downhill ski. The one the teacher sees through, but is too tired to argue with.

The one alone.
In the middle of the field.
In giant snowshoes.
Pretending that it's just as fun, if not more, than downhill skiing.

Sometimes I wonder what would've happened if I hadn't just…*fallen over.* If I had swallowed my fear and gone down the hill. Would it have changed the course of my life? Would I be someone else today?

My mother (a fearless woman who is constantly baffled by my ineptitude to navigate our city's most beloved season) thinks the fear started with the death of my father who never came home after hitting a patch of ice on the QE2.

But I would never say that.

I would never blame my problems, my shortcomings, my debilitating, existential fears on my father.
Instead I blame her. I believe it started when she sent me to an ill-equipped babysitter who was more than happy to let me run wild.

It was just after I learned to walk. I spent most of my toddler years on all fours. I knew how to walk, I just didn't want to. Perhaps I felt safer being closer to the ground. But finally, when I'm three, I start walking on a regular basis. It's the end of summer, and by fall I'm ripping around like I own the place and by winter nothing can stop me.

At least that's what I think.

It's a perfect day (in my memory, anyway.) Bright and sunny, not too much wind. The kind of winter day our hopes and dreams are built on. I'm at my babysitter's house, playing outside with my life-size doll, Suzie. Not only do Suzie and I have the audacity to run around on a winter day, we have the audacity to run around without a care in the world.

Until it happens:

We slip. *I* slip. Hit a patch of ice and my legs fly out from under me. I slam on my back just in time to see Suzie, bless her soul, slam face first into the snowbank.

I'm in shock. Obviously, I've fallen plenty of times. But not like this. I have never been taken by surprise quite like this. In my three-year-old mind, it's an injustice of epic proportions, and it teaches me a valuable lesson: winter is not to be messed with.

At the hospital they say my leg is fractured. All I know is that I'll have a cast for the next eight weeks.

So much for walking.
So much for winter.
So much for being without a care in the world.

My mother, unlike me, is a "get back on the horse" kind of person. Therefore she doesn't understand my reluctance to go outside the next winter. She also doesn't think it will last.

"Children have memories like goldfish," she used to say.

So she really can't comprehend my horror a year later when she takes me down to Hawrelak Park for what I think will be hot chocolate and a sleigh ride, and instead turns into her pulling out what looks like knives sewn onto a pair of boots and declaring:

"It's time you learned how."

And then, without hearing my opinion, she straps skates to my feet and pulls me onto the frozen pond. I stand there like a four-foot sack of frozen potatoes, forcing her to support me. She pulls me along, loop after loop begging me to move my feet. But my feet won't move. My body won't move. All I can do is cling to her for dear life. I wait, beg, pray for the courage to pry my small fingers off of her arm, but it doesn't come.

Finally, after seven exhausting spins around the large body of water, we stop. She lets me go. I fall. This scenario repeats itself every Saturday for the next four months. Eventually, finally, just before the ice starts to melt, she gives up.

But I don't get off so easy.

My mother decides that I am simply trying to defy her, so she enlists her co-worker Sandy to teach me. The sun beats down on us as Sandy, a heavy set woman in her fifties, leads me down to the small pond on her acreage.

I eye Sandy with an uneasy feeling in my stomach. More uneasy than usual. We take one step onto the ice and that's when I'm sure I hear it—

Crack.
I look at Sandy. No reaction.
Crack.
There it is again.
I should warn her.
But I don't.
Instead, I do what any self-respecting five-year-old would do—
Run.

My feet finally moving, I skate as fast as I can, trying to get as far away from Sandy as possible.

"You're skating!" She cries.

I'm skating? I'm skating. *I'm* skating!

A miracle! I have triumphed over this season! I belong in this city! I have joined the chorus of winter-lovers!
Crack.
Thud.
Sploosh.

Sandy has gone through the ice. I guess I should've warned her.
I turn just in time to see her arms flailing. Her husband running.
I stare at her.
Frozen.
Once again unable to move my feet.

What a cruel joke winter has played on Sandy.
What a cruel joke winter has played on me.

I refuse to go skating again.

The next year, during the winter carnival, I accept a dare from the class know-it-all, and, in doing so, get my tongue stuck to a metal post. The fire department is called in to rescue me as my classmates watch on. The following year I pretend to have the seven-year-old's version of fibromyalgia in order to avoid winter activities altogether.

The year after that however, I decide to "man up," so to speak. Take matters into my own hands. Find a new winter activity that doesn't involve icicles, walking on ice, skating on ice, or ice of any kind.

Sledding.

Sledding would be my new winter sport. As soon as the first snowfall hits, I start training. And a month later when Mr. Walker announces he's taking us to Rundle Park on a sledding field trip, it's like, THE BEST THING EVER. I'll be able to show off my skills, prove my winter prowess. I immediately feel myself climbing the ranks of the social structure.

The day starts out perfectly. I'm fearless. I go over all the jumps the boys do, I never once wipe out, I'm totally in control.

Until I'm not.

It had been over an hour of running up and down that hill, and it was time for a break. Not only was my face frozen and my tummy grumbling, but I needed to pee like nobody's business.

But just as I'm about to walk away—
I see him.
Curtis Ferguson.
The cutest boy in class and he's walking right towards me.

He asks if we can double on my fluorescent pink saucer. How can I say no? I nod my head and erupt into a fit of nervous giggles. Nothing like this has ever happened to me before.

He folds up his limbs and squeezes onto the saucer as I laugh harder and harder. I'm laughing so hard that I'm not able to protest when he says: "Ready?"

I'm not able to say: "No, give me a second!"
I'm not able to gain my composure.
Breathe.
Get control.

I'm not able to do anything but laugh, so off we go. As he flings us down the hill, I'm laughing and laughing and my position isn't right and I already have to go to the bathroom, and I can't stop laughing and—

No...no....no...no…no...nonononono NO!
I feel it running down my leg.
I can't control it.
We're going too fast.
Each time we hit a bump it's like a geyser erupting.

When we get to the bottom we both look down at my pink saucer now filled with liquid. We look at each other.

Oh no…Curtis…don't do this… please don't do this—
"Sick! Mary peed on the sled!"
He yells it at the top of his lungs. Everybody clears away and that's when I know.

My sledding days are over.

For the next two years I do everything I can to avoid winter. Activities, conversations, festivals, art projects. My friends throw birthday parties in which they go ice fishing. I tell them my family doesn't believe in birthday parties. We're Jehovah's Witnesses. But only in winter.

But then…
it's 1988.
The Winter Olympics.

The Olympics breeds insanity at the best of times. Businesses are shut down in the afternoon, bars are open at 10am, families bring televisions into the kitchen, parents would gladly sell off their children for two tickets to the gold medal hockey game.

But imagine if the Olympics were hosted in your province, only three hours away from where you live. That's 1988. The Olympics on steroids. It's all anyone talks about. And for a kid who is trying to avoid winter and all it entails… it's hell.

So I pretend it's not happening.
That I don't care.
That I'm too cool for *The Olympics.*

And when the entire school is called into the gymnasium and told that one person from each class will be picked to run through the city with the Olympic Torch—I pretend not to pay any attention.

As we go through each class, the teacher pulling a name randomly out of a pail, I pretend that my heart isn't beating a million miles a second. That my hands aren't sweating. I pretend to be fascinated by the bouncy ball my friend Marcia got out of the twenty-five cent machine at Safeway the night before.

Bounce…
Bounce…
Bounce…

They get to my class. Mrs. Tracy reaches her hand into the pail.

Bounce…
She pulls out a piece of paper.
Bounce…
She opens it up.
Bounce…

Mary Friesen.
Bou-
Mary Friesen?
nce....
Mary Friesen!

The ball rolls away.
Mary Friesen!!
She keeps repeating it.
I won't move.
All eyes are on me. The entire school. Watching.
I still won't move.

She starts to make wild arm movements in my direction.
I consider my options. What could happen if I run with the torch:
What if I can't keep up?
What if my hand freezes to it?
What if I fall? On national television!
What if I set myself on fire?
What if I set another student on fire?
What if... what if Elizabeth Manley is there and I set her on fire?!
I can definitely not run with the torch. Think of all the—

"I will run with the torch Mrs. Tracy."
Feroz Fulbin.
Top student.
Suck up.
Lover of all things winter.
"Thank you, Feroz," says Mrs. Tracy.
And like a hero, Feroz walks to the front of the gymnasium and every-
body cheers.

One week later Feroz walked through Edmonton with the Olympic
Torch.
And
I

did
not.

And all I could think about was how proud my father would have been.

———————

"Auntieeeeeeeeee. Come on!"

My niece is waving at me from the other side of the parking lot. She made it across while I stood here frozen.

"What are you so scared of?" she asks.

I contemplate her question. It's much bigger than she could ever realize.

What am I scared of?
The unexpected. The unknown. The uncontrollable.
I feel a kick inside my belly.
Perhaps it's time to embrace those things.
I'm tired of missing the view.

And I certainly don't want my niece or my daughter, who will be born in just a few short months, to ever miss it either.

I take a step.
And then another.
I pause.
And without any shame, I get down on all fours.

I'll make it across the parking lot, the skating rink as it were, but I'll do it my way.

"I'm coming," I say. And I start to crawl.

DOG DAYS OF WINTER

SUSAN TOKARIUK

(Alternate title: *The Insanity of Nearly Freezing Your "You Know Whats" Off Raising and Racing Sled Dogs For Some Intangible Reward That Has Something To Do With the Inexplicable Bond Between Man, Dog and Old Man Winter*)

Meet Ivan, the sled dog, who in less time than it takes to say, "Are you hungry, boy?", inhales 64 ounces of dog slop (raw meat, liver-baited, fat-infused, kibble crunch, warm-watered "mushers mix"). He's also the dog whose instinctual doggy dinner alarm clock renders my personal alarm clock useless. And the dog whose salivary glands mobilize at the mere sight of his empty dog dish thereby helping to prove Pavlov's theory while concurrently inspiring dreadful images of Stephen King's rabies infested, foam-mouthed Cujo.

You know it's cold in Edmonton when:

Ivan, the King of Consumption, refuses to leave the warmth of his dog house until the food is actually in the dish, but not before he has desperately strained to reach the food from the comforts of his naturally heated home.

That's when you know it's cold.

No one, or nothing, is more primal or singularly dedicated to satisfying his bodily desires as our dog, Ivan. So when his survival instincts cause him to re-evaluate his...well...um... other survival instincts, then something is amiss. Witnessing the hesitation from the comforts of my own centrally heated acreage home southeast of the city gives me ~~paws~~ pause for thought. It's not that cold, is it? It certainly is if Ivan's any indication. He's actually dancing on the packed snow as he eats, as if he's afraid he might freeze his paws to the ground if he pauses for one second. But hey, he *did* emerge for the *five* vital seconds necessary to inhale *nine hours* of sustenance, which, I might note, is not a bad return on his time investment.

But all that aside, I did (and still do) worry about our team staying warm when "Old Man Winter", with the vengeance of Robert DeNiro chastising Ben Stiller, *mano a mano,* in *Meet the Fockers,* undiplomatically returns the words "respect" and "humility" to our vocabulary. Philosophically speaking, only an old man would have the gonads to demand such concepts from the younger generation in this day and age. Speaking of which, my husband, Wes, is probably freezing his gonads off while Ivan, given his survival instincts, is probably warming his up in a manner that most men envy. I shouldn't minimize Ivan's concern for the well-being of the family jewels, though. It wasn't too long ago, a few years back if I recall correctly, that he *did* almost lose them to a minor case of frostbite.

Now that was cold!

Fort Nelson, on the river, felt like −10,000 degrees with the wind chill, and then when the filming crew flew over the staging area in a helicopter, even the thought of being on television wasn't enough to make up for the added "rotor chill" factor. Not fun. In fact, if I recall correctly, the experience was so traumatizing that, when a colleague back home informed me that he saw me on television, I wasn't even remotely snobbish about my new-found fame. "How'd you even recognize me beneath my Helly Hansen's?" I asked, half joking and half credulous at being noticed at all (seriously, who watches PBS?). Meanwhile, I was sending silent prayers of thanks to the demi-God, Helly Hansen himself, for founding the Norwegian company and designing the hardcore winter work wear that concealed all but my eyes.

It was seriously cold that day, I tell you.

"Actually, I recognized your dog truck. Looked like you were scooping dog poop, or something," he replied, deadpan. Now that's just perfect. Couldn't they have filmed the part where I was devotedly dragging Wes's team to the starting line and then added a voice-over acknowledging how dedicated and supportive the spouses/dog-handlers are in the face of natural adversities?

To be honest, much of the filming did, indeed, portray and acknowledge the dedication of every participant. And for the record, my short contribution to the documentary actually portrayed me harnessing and petting our dog team in preparation for their race (Note to self: ignore all colleagues when they lie to your face about your television debut. They're just jealous.).

In reality, a million negative degrees couldn't have put a damper on anyone's spirit. That was the big race. All the small-town, big-name mushers were there. And the temperature only added to the already intense challenge.

One thing that's forever true about mushing, whether you are a local legend or a no-name Edmonton musher: It's always a race against the elements—snow conditions, trail conditions, how well you've prepared your team, whether a dog has to stop and take a dump in the middle of the race. Yup, it's the natural elements that determine the outcome. The musher is simply weight on the back of the sled, ballast as it were, something to slow the dogs down and sometimes a soft voice of encouragement to keep them going, though they hardly need it.

Wes, my no-name musher, was not concerned about "rotor chill" or any other kind of chill that day. He was eager to measure his team's talent against many of the best sprint racers in the nation. Unfortunately, he didn't fare well that day, and neither did Ivan with the frostbite thingy, but they both retained their respective man-parts in regards to the challenge of the sport. Wes's man-parts may have even grown a little—figuratively, of course—in the process. Whose wouldn't after surviving cold like that?

Ah…if only someone could harness the positive energy and enthusiasm of a dog sled team…and then give it to me on an Alberta winter day. Ivan's manhood survived that race and Wes learned a valuable lesson about manning up in the face of a real challenge.

That's the beauty of accepting and surviving the extreme adversity that wraps itself innocently in a crisp, white blanket of deception and lures young and old alike to dare to mar the perfection. Mushers and downhill skiers are the only people on earth who welcome the challenge of a fresh snowfall, though the downhill skiers demonstrate their determination vertically, whereas sprint racers tend to remain relatively horizontal as they trail blaze (there's an inappropriately kickass good t-shirt design and catchphrase in there somewhere: "Mushers do it…like dogs? …with dogs?" No, neither of those is quite right.).

Regarding mushing, there are definitely better and more appropriate sayings on t-shirts, like: "Only fools go where angels fear to sled." Mushers tend to disagree, but only with the "fools" part. Not being ~~the~~ fools ~~that they are~~, they probably prefer to quote Confucius: "It does not matter how slowly you go as long as you do not stop." Actually, I just made that up, not the idiom (Confucius did say that), but the part about knowing a musher's preference. I've never heard a musher quote anyone but another musher, so they must prefer to make up their own sayings. For example, Wes's favorite way to describe sprint racing is, and I quote: "A balls out race to the finish" (and Ivan wouldn't disagree with the "balls out" part).

Sprint racing is not to be confused with distance racing. That would be like comparing Ben Johnson to a marathon racer, or like comparing the Edmonton Sled Dog Classic from years back to the Iditarod. Two different athletes. Two different distances. Two different lifestyles altogether. The Iditarod is like being married to mushing, whereas sprint racing is more like…well, it's more like being in a common-law relationship with mushing. Either way, come hell or heavy snowfall warning, you have to train the team.

Maybe the difference really comes down to where the musher sleeps. The distance musher sleeps with his dogs on the trail, but he is not necessarily "in the doghouse" in respect to his relationship with his wife. Whereas the sprint musher usually rents a cheap hotel room or gets relegated to the bottom bunk bed of somebody's spare bedroom separated from his wife/dog-handler who gets the top bunk and is seriously considering encouraging her partner to take up distance racing while she tries to ignore the fact that all of the glowing, green planets on the ceiling above her (and her own cosmic stars) are somehow seriously misaligned. The "wife chill" factor (otherwise known as "the cold shoulder") is definitely a concern for the sprint musher.

Now if we're talking Iditarod or the Yukon Quest or any other distance race, we're talking cold. Yet these races hold some strange attraction to men like Wes, men built to endure. His idea of a dream vacation is to volunteer his time to fly into some remote village north of 60, in a four-seater propeller plane borrowed from the set of Arctic Air, with Adam Beach as his pilot. Just so he can break bread with the locals while he waits for days (consisting of an average of, what…one or two minutes of sunlight per day?) in order to catch a glimpse of Lance Mackey or Martin Buser, or one of their heirs to the Iditarod throne. Those who continue in the family tradition as they shush-shush-shush through a check stop in a near state of delirium brought on by sleep deprivation, and the only souvenirs available are frozen doggie droppings and used booties.

"Wouldn't that be awesome, honey?!"

Outside voice: "Oh yeah! You should go for it, for sure."

Inside voice: Are you kidding? You're talking Arctic Circle. I'm thinking equator—zero degrees—latitude. You've heard of it, haven't you? No? I think I have to get my hair frosted that day.

Speaking of frosting, in the short time that Wes has been out feeding the dogs, he's acquired an appropriately frosted muzzle that would rival any old man's, winter or otherwise. But this doesn't phase him. In fact, I think it might be a rite of passage within the musher's circle, or might give him the right to participate in the one-upping rituals that occur at the musher's banquet on Saturday nights.

Musher #1: "It was so cold that the ice from my mustache froze to the ice on my soul patch and I couldn't give my leaders any commands! Lucky thing my lead dog, Axel, is so smart and could read my mind and got us across the finish line."

Me (aside, under my breath): "Lucky Axel can follow the scent of the team in front of him. They say a dog's olfactory senses are pretty... well...sensitive."

Musher #2: "That's nothing! This one race I was at was so cold that my hands literally froze to the sled. I had to pry them off with the snow hook and then ride with no hands while I warmed them up in my pants. Finished the race in third place that way and almost got frost-bite you know where.

Me (*aside, under my breath*): "Lucky for you it didn't end in a quick trip to the vet for a quick snip snip. Ivan knows what I'm talking about."

Musher #3 (Wes): "That's nothing! You gotta hear about my run last weekend at the Blackfoot. We're a couple miles from the truck when I see this moose off to the right knowing my team's supposed to go left. Well hell, they see the damn thing and shift into warp five! Left half of my sled wrapped around the tree I hit on the corner. When I wasn't being dragged, I was trying to stand on one runner. My brake was useless. Packed my snow pants and every known orifice with snow, so I know what you mean about being frozen solid, I tell you! And about that frostbite thingy, Ivan just about lost *his* "you know whats" to frost-bite a few years back when...blah, blah, blah."

Me (*aside, under my breath*): "Lucky for me I married a musher or I'd have missed all this and would have otherwise been subjected to the boredom of normal holidays spent reading *50 Shades of Grey* or *Twilight* on a beach in Mexico."

But I have to give them their props. They're making the best of a worst case scenario and I know that they weren't actually *enjoying* them-selves while their various body parts were slowly solidifying (they weren't, were they?). They are men who man up in the face of physical adversity. They are bonding with each other in the only way they know how—by one-upping each other.

But what ungraciously appears as bragging is really something far more sincere and heartfelt in disguise. It is the sharing of a primal and singularly dedicated bond they each have with their respective dogs. True "dog people" know what I'm talking about (if you don't own a dog and can't really call yourself a true "dog person," then imagine the bond between…hmmm…let's say, a man and the remote). And that bond, the one between musher and dog, makes for a mighty powerful contender when winter pulls out all the stops. It's a bond powerful enough to drive a musher to do anything for his dogs: freeze his "you know whats" off, choose sleep deprivation or a DNF by his name over the chance of an injury, or return to the Antarctic against all hope because nobody gets left behind as was the case depicted in the film *Eight Below*.

Wes, once, Did Not Finish a race, and he was devastated. Not because of the DNF, but because sometimes the coldest, darkest days have nothing to do with the temperature. His lead dog, Jerry, collapsed and died less than two miles into a six mile race while doing what they both loved with a passion—running the race. Recovery from this devastating loss was questionable. Jerry was the heart and soul of the team. But dogs have an uncanny way of helping us put the "man" in the phrase "man up".

A photographer forwarded a picture he had taken of the team mere seconds prior to Jerry's collapse. It was the steely determination caught in the glint of a pair of ice blue eyes that triggered the first step in a long and arduous uphill climb. Having six of Jerry's pups (four with ice blue eyes) didn't hurt either. Wes began to see shades of Jerry everywhere. What he really saw was hope and perpetuity. Life moves forward and so do we, even when the trail takes us through the coldest, darkest dog days of winter. Sometimes, it just takes us a little longer to complete a more challenging journey. Wes eventually recovered from Jerry's noticeable absence and literally climbed a mountain to win his first race—post-Jerry.

This sport called mushing is a metaphor for life. It's all about one's ability to endure the harshest conditions and refuse to quit the journey. It could be a sprint race or the Iditarod; it could be north of 60 or the South Pole; or it could be in my no-name backyard outside of Edmonton, Alberta when it is so cold that even Ivan is almost tempted to forego his dinner and remain in his house. But he doesn't succumb. He leaves the comfort of a cozy bed to do what he does second best—eat, so that he can fortify himself to do what he does best—run the race.

It doesn't matter the distance or where the race takes place, or the fact that the details of every race differ. What matters is that we endure the journey and make it to the musher's banquet where we can feast and proudly brag about the time we stared Old Man Winter in the face (albeit, squinting through frost-laden eyelashes) and didn't flinch.

MOON CALLING

DON PERKINS

For most of a year, I shared a hallway with Richard Van Camp: Writer-in-Residence to the Department of English and Film Studies at the U of A, and an infectiously positive, eternally cheering, irrepressibly encouraging presence. Every month, there would be the ceremonial,"Happy full moon," in joyful bellow as he passed by.

One week he was especially charged up by a spectacularly beautiful display, the kind you get on the prairies under a February arctic high pressure system—skies clear all the way to the edge of the universe. That morning, 6:20 a.m., and George the dog and I had been out in the trampled snow paths between the farm fields on the University of Alberta South Campus, walking briskly into the full glow of the moon angling towards the horizon to the west. Under these conditions, we cast moon shadows—more like shadows of shadows.

But, for all I have to admit the full moon bright in the face is an enchantment, I'm not a Richard. For me, the magic is in that tiny, insistent sliver of the new moon, just making its way briefly up the early evening western sky not long after nightfall. It is at its best, too, in winter, when the snow cover reflects a faint light back up and creates that spectral effect of the "new moon with the old moon in her arms." Just that little celestial fingernail clipping, cradling the fullness of what was and is to come (and go) again in that eternal lunar meta-phor for life's cycles.

Yes, the monthly "coming of age" brilliance of the full moon is invigorating, even hypnotic.

But that moment of the infant embracing its own future ripeness, that's the moon that calls.

HER SAINTS ALIGNED

JON LEPPARD

Ancient wisdom shuffles forward
Eyes downcast
Seeking the crack that waits
Like a baited trap
Waiting to shatter her bones
Her bones, thin as the communion wafer
That broke her fast
But will not break the fall
She knows is coming

It's winter she fears most
Changer of terrains
Keeper of the dangerous angels
"How can I move any slower?"
She asks the graying day
"Stay in, stay in, stay safe."
Whisper the fallen saints

Yet still she ventures forth
The carnivorous prairie wind
Finds precious little sustenance
In the parchment of her face

She seeks an ice-free passage
From pew to coffee shop
Her blueberry muffin
And a man who says, "Hello."

FIRST ON JASPER

JON LEPPARD

Jasper and 4th and my focus is down
Down on my feet
Down as in town

Buses and cars chase each other around
Sticky old eyes
Glued to the ground

Tickle me this as a snowflake lands
Like a whisper upon
The back of my hand

Flurry and fling...Boy, it's still good to know
My tongue hasn't lost
Its knowing of snow

TRANSLATING TWILIGHT, JANUARY

JANNIE EDWARDS

The feathered hour. The Muse of brooding
presses the snarled, tender genealogies.

Light slurs from golden
to the blue afterlight of ash.

Ghost cellos murmur a purred, bruised brogue—
moth harmonics.

Brain takes down the familiar letters again, dismantling
the small anniversaries of shadows

the way one shakes a watch
that has stopped working.

The old cat curls asleep on an open book
about the secret life of elephants.

LEARNING TO DRIVE - LAKE WABAMUN 1961

JOAN SHILLINGTON

You needed someone to edge the jeep forward
while you loaded wood on the red trailer
told me to dress warm and grabbed two pillows
to prop me closer. Gearshift set in first gear,
you showed me how to release the clutch, inch
forward in that rusty vehicle with plastic windows,
crankcase heavy and stubborn in the cold.
I lurched and stalled more times than forward
and you ballooned the day with expletives
best left for a barroom or brawl. Remember,
it was Sunday morning, snow blinding white,
deep over my thighs and so cold it would freeze
a witch's tit you said but we stomped through
the bush and piled wood on that trailer, the sun
a peculiar brilliant peeking through winter branches,
watching us, watching me, eleven years old,
fall in love with gearshifts, wheels, axles and cars.

LUNGS

MICHELLE NANCY KENNEDY

You sit on the porch. Shivering. I feel like your bones might crumble with the next shudder of cold and anticipation. I pull on my parka and open the door:

"Come inside. It's too cold."

You look at me through icicle lashes and I know it's a silly request. You have to wait. It's too important not to witness the entire frigid event.

"Jacket?"

You roll your eyes at me and I smile, pull your jacket off the hook, hand it to you and close the door. I watch you through the window as you struggle to zip the coat up. Your eyes never leave the drive and mine never leave your cheeks.

How quickly the tears would freeze if you were disappointed again. How I would pray you were warm again, shivering beside me long into the night.

I sweat in my parka staring out the window and feel instantly guilty. I pull on my boots, a scarf, a pair of those little 99 cent gloves and warmer mittens and step outside. Now we're waiting outside. It's February and it's cold. Jesus Christ it's cold. I can't breathe because my lungs hurt:

"My lungs hurt."

And you just chuckle quietly because everyone is cold and everyone's lungs hurt and I'm not even the last person who will complain about the weather to you today. I guess that's what happens when you work in retail. People complain about their lungs aching in the winter.

I know you worry that I'll judge you for working in retail but I love you because you only shave on Wednesdays and even though you never ever brush your hair it always looks perfect. Besides, I think it's important that you sell people lozenges and stamps and charge them for a bag. You're saving them, a little bit. I always tell you this and you always laugh at me.

So there we are, on the porch, our lungs aching, but we stand and wait.

Together. Me, worrying. You, waiting for your dad. It's been years and he'll likely complain about the weather too. He has even older lungs than me or you. And for all we know he's been in a place where his lungs never hurt, where they were warm and full of hot air every single moment he was away.

I wonder what your 4-day-old bearded smile will look like when you see him after all these years. I wonder if the tears will stay warm on your cheeks and if his cool breath will leave icicles on your beard.

"My lungs hurt."

CONVERSATION

KY PERRAUN

The five-ton lumbers through the 28 cm of snow
that has fallen in the last 36 hours. You are careful
to leave 10 metres between you and the vehicle ahead,
knowing an accident occurs in a split second, no time
to think, it's all automatic when the shit hits the fan.

I'm at home, watching the word count grow as I type.
I wait for your call the way a nesting bird waits
for a beak full of seed. Heat hums in the small rooms.

'Call from seven eight zero, six eight six, one four
nine three,' the voice calls out, nasal and monotone.

'Hi sweetie,' iced wipers, gritty on cold glass, chant
their fricative song.

It is November 9, 2012, 8:30 a.m. It is minus five
outside, 23 above indoors. Our conversation lasts
17 minutes before the line goes dead, words frozen
in air.

I'M A HOUSEPLANT

MICHAEL HAMM

Call me old-fashioned, but I think houseplants should die in the winter.

All my mother's houseplants died in the winter. All my grandmother's houseplants died in the winter. It's natural. As natural as me forgetting to take a houseplant down from the freezing window sill, as natural as me forgetting to water a houseplant. That's what I'm trying to say. You don't have to do anything. You do *nothing,* and the plant dies. Nature. Left to its own devices, a houseplant will die in the winter. Nature. Like some kind of idiot-plant. Nature.

I'm a houseplant. I do nothing, and die every winter.

Some people embrace winter. This October I saw these people gathered on 104th Street. There was hot chocolate and a fire and people making speeches. It was all to try to inspire people to get outside and embrace winter, but I didn't know that at the time. I just drove by them and thought, "those dear poor homeless people."

I don't embrace winter. I don't even brace *for* winter. I ignore winter.

For example, it's almost January and I don't have a toque. I thought I had one somewhere, but I haven't been able to find it or get around to trying to find it. I've ignored winter so well that I've almost made it all the way through without having to spend five minutes buying something that would make my entire head feel better for the next four months. I do have a glove though. I found it at the Kinsmen and now I put it on when I need to put gas in my car. My other hand goes in my pocket. My entire head freezes solid. It's not the best system but it's my system.

I think everyone should have a library card, because you never know when you're going to need something to scrape your windshield with when your three dollar scraper breaks. I bought the three dollar scraper because I thought sixteen dollars was an absurd amount of money to spend on something I would use every day for half of the year, every year from now until I die (any year now).

I'm trying to change. I know a lot of people say that a man can't change, but I have a deep, golden, powerful faith that a man can buy a second glove.

I almost bought one the other day when I was at MEC. I love MEC. I like to go there and look at all the outdoorsy stuff. I love outdoorsy stuff. It makes me feel outdoorsy. It makes me feel outdoorsy while (this is key) allowing my body to remain in the warm and wonderful indoorsey of the MEC building. If MEC didn't have a warm and wonderful indoorsey, and was instead some sort of open-air market, I would never go. I wouldn't even know what a MEC was. I would drive by and think, "those dear poor homeless people."

I've been going to MEC enough for it to influence me. I know things about knives and base layers and chalk bags. When I see a cool ice pick I don't immediately think, "imagine ice-picking a person's head." I think, "imagine ice-picking some ice." The other day I bought a flint and steel. I used it to light some toilet paper on fire in my bathtub.

But I'm going to buy a bike next. They have these really neat bikes at MEC and I have this plan to take the insurance off my car and bike to work this summer. I'm so excited to buy this bike. I wish I could start now, but it's still winter and really only crazy people ride their bikes in the winter.

The two crazy people I know who ride their bikes in the winter are my friend Davis and my neighbour Mike.

Davis is a winter guy. And a summer guy. He's extremely both. Those two seasons define his world. He's all about winter beers and winter music and summer movies and summer dishes with summery summer squash salad. Every winter he's out and about in his one thousand dollar Helly Hansen jacket and every summer he's out and about in a pair of shin-length shorts and nothing else. The only times he's not around a lot are spring and fall. I think he uses this time to transform. It will be September and I'll be like, "Where's Davis?" and then Davis bursts through my door wearing snowshoes and sporting a full beard and talking about how he just finished winterizing his urban hybrid bike but still needs to get the disc brakes looked at or whatever.

Mike doesn't ride a cool urban hybrid MEC bike with disc brakes. He rides a normal bike, the kind a middle-age blue collar dude would ride home, with bags of groceries hanging from the handlebars. The first time I met Mike was when I was moving into the building and he popped his head out into the hall to see who I was. He was chewing raw spaghetti. He shook my hand and now we're neighbours.

I think Mike ignores winter, too. But not in the cowardly stupid dumb-head way I do. In a sensible, practical way. A two-gloves kind of way. When it's cold, he puts on a coat. When it's warm, he doesn't. He rides his bike in the winter but not because he's winterized, but because that's how he gets around, even if there happens to be snow today. He honestly might not know what month of the year it is. The guy could be trapped in a sort of amnesia-state, stuck somewhere around his 29th birthday for all I know. I swear he once asked me if I was worried about Y2K.

I'm trying to change. I'm not sure if I'll ever be able to embrace winter like Davis or those homeless people on 104th Street. Maybe I'll just learn to ignore it better. But I need to do something. I can't stay inside doing nothing and dying like a houseplant, or feeling outdoorsy inside MEC or pumping gas with one glove and a frozen head. I have to go outside. I want to ice-pick a waterfall and see if it feels like I imagine.

PROWLER

MYRNA GARANIS

It's winter, well past eleven, my nightly glance out back
for who else isn't tucked in bed. And there she is,
low-slung cat, black on the fresh dusting, loping
coyote-like down the neighbour's driveway.

She's set off their garage door sensor, a shaggy shape
silhouetted in yellow light for forty-five seconds.
Unfazed, she carries on, follows the shoveled path.

I, curious cat, switch windows, trail her
from the comfort of indoors. Out there, minus 30
with wind. The cat doesn't hurry. Her pace
is steady, full of purpose. She reaches the front walk.
Barely hesitates before crossing the deserted street.

She could be pregnant, her coat so thick,
so confident a door will swing open.

COUNTERCLOCKWISE AT VICTORIA OVAL

SHIRLEY SERVISS

Skating in the city in my father's hereford sweater,
its warm hug holds me tight like his grip on my mitten
as I learned to glide on two thin blades,
slide my scissor feet, cutting lines in the ice.
Sounds of traffic and sirens replace the Strauss waltzes that crackled
on the stereo while fire crackled
in the coal heater to warm cold toes.

I skate counterclockwise this Sunday afternoon,
as he taught me so long ago, skate backwards in time to all those
winter nights he tightened our laces,
visited with other parents as we played
tag and crack-the-whip, crashed into boards.
Skate backwards to the spring we sailed
on flooded fields frozen as far as the horizon.

Speed skaters snap past outside the blue line,
remind me of bonspiels—only one sheet of ice
left for us to race the rocks past the hog line.
Treats of hot dogs and every kind of pie
made by our mothers, sold for nickels and dimes.
Our own mother transformed into an athlete—
trading house dress and apron for woolen pants and tam,
sweeping the ice, urging rocks into the house
with her broom.

WINTER DOGS

ALICIA CHRISTIANSON

I

the animal's throat lets out a loud breath
it lingers, eager paws dug into the black earth, while

snow smothers the city into silence
with a wide, white fist

II

this animal buries as many bones before
the snow stops our graveyard from growing

yet she digs for fish among the frost and rocks
of an emptied pond

III

the animal smoothed against my leg leaves
in its wake an icy, choking ghost

turning, her frozen snout burns me, brands me
every time I let winter in

NO WINTER

BRAD KENNEDY

i am withdrawing into my hoodie like a turtle into its shell
and i am pretending i am in a cave
and the cave is far away and not on this bus
with this city skittering by outside the windows
and from the inside of my cave i am texting you so that you can be in
here too
just us, warm, in the cave
no winter

THE JOY OF WINTER

GARRY GARRISON

In the dark and dead of deep December,
the sleepy sun on southern holiday,
city snowed in until the first of May,
normal people moan and bitch and whimper
the slippery-sidewalk-bitter-wind-flu-
car-won't-start-fender-bender-nasal-drip-
pre-Christmas-mall-trudge-Mexico-wish-trip-
snow shoveling-shivering-blizzard blues.

But Jasmine walks, skis, snowshoes, skates, dances
a hoar-frosted sparkling ice crystal swirl
minus 30 jubilee. "Wake up world!
I'm 50, cancer-free. Many more chances
to make friends, savour each day and season.
I'm alive! Don't need another reason."

COLD HATE

MAUREEN SMALL

I'm miserable. I'm angry. I hate it. I hate the stinging cold on my face. I hate the way my fingertips hurt inside my gloves. I hate the ugly grey landscape. I hate the pain in my sinuses and the earache from the wind. I hate the Facebook statuses that say, "I LOVE winter!"

What is there to love about this? Don't give me crap about cozy, warm fires, candles and Christmas. Christmas will come whether you live in Namibia or Texas or Maui. Snow does not equal Christmas. Fire and candles? Of course they're wonderful—because they're inside. That's my whole point: what's to love about winter outside in Edmonton?

I don't hate snow. When I was a child on the West Coast, snow made me giddy. We sledded. We built snowmen and snow forts and made snowballs to throw at each other. We didn't have to go to school. "Cold" was −5, and in three days it was all over. I love snow.

I love snowstorms. Even the ones in Edmonton. Especially the ones in Edmonton. I love the build up of excitement—it's coming! The mother of all snowstorms! They're calling for 30 cm in the next 12 hours. It's going to be chaos. We'll be trending on Twitter. There will be cars sliding down 105th Street and littering the ditches of the Anthony Henday. It will be gloriously exciting. We'll watch the snow piling up on the fence outside the office and chatter with wide-eyed wonder about how we'll ever get home. We'll talk to strangers on the bus and strangers in Canadian Tire, and we'll talk to our neighbours as we dig out our sidewalk. We're all in this together and everyone is my friend.

Then the storm ends, the pretty white snow is violated by rough, brown dirt, and the temperature plummets in proportion to the rising of the wind. This is what I hate—the cold. The wind. I go back to trudging with my head down, only my teary eyes exposed beneath layers of scarf, hat, hood and earmuffs. No more camaraderie. No more playfulness. Sledding? Too frickin' cold. Snowmen? Can't pack the bloody stuff. Snow forts? Snowballs? Snow angels? Ha! Not when it's 40 below.

I love a tropical beach, and I can tell you why, too. I love the feel of the warm sun on my skin and sand between my toes. I love the sound of the breeze on the tops of the palm trees and of the waves lapping at the shore. I love the ease of throwing on sandals, a tank top and shorts. I love that wherever I look at any time of day or night, I see beauty that takes my breath away. Specific, tangible feelings, sights and sounds together make up what I love about a tropical beach.

So you love winter in Edmonton? What specifically do you love about it? The wind biting your face? Changing your footwear every time you leave or enter your home and office? Scraping your windshield? Or is it the sound of the wind howling through your ears? The ache of your teeth? The way your neck and shoulders immediately tense up when you step outside?

My friends say it's the hot chocolate they love, and skating and skiing and riding horses in the snow. Hayrides and sleigh rides and frost on the trees. Sledding and snowmen and snowballs. It's wondrous and magical, special and pretty, they tell me. Perhaps I'd think so too if I lived inside a Christmas card picture. But I'm standing at the gas pump, fingers numb, toes numb, nose numb. Fingers hurt, toes hurt, nose hurts. Odd how I can be numb and in pain at the same time. The wind whips my hair into my eyes, my pant legs swirl around my ankles, and I'm shaking in spite of my winter coat. My friend Angela advised me how to dress for winter: long johns, several layers of warm pants, warm mittens, neck muffler, nice warm hat. Well, yes, if I'm going sledding. But I'm going to work. And then the post office. And the grocery store. And the dreaded gas station. I want to throw on my raincoat and just GO. I want to leisurely hop in and out of my car. I want it to actually be warmer in my car than it is outside. I want to spend more time running errands than getting dressed to run them. I want to be able to live in 40 below, not just *play* in it.

Can I acclimatize? Are people born with a love for certain climates? Do we gravitate to what we were raised in? When it's +32 in July, my

African-born friend gushes, "Isn't it a beautiful day?" while my Alberta-born husband grumbles and sweats. Given a choice of 30 above or 30 below, he'll take the cold any day. Rain doesn't bother me. Eighty-nine days straight of drizzle—I grew up with that. I feel all ChristmasSy when the streetlights shine off the slick roads in the dark at 4:30pm. I wonder though…after enduring six Edmonton winters, would I still pay no heed to the rain? Or like all the Albertans I've known who transplanted to the "wet" coast, would I long again for the cold but sunshiney days of prairie winters?

I try to conjure up fond memories of winter in Edmonton. Walking my dog and letting him run at the off-leash park. It's cold, crisp, and getting dark. My head is down, bundled into my old Helly Hansen parka. With my scarf covering my nose and mouth, my glasses fog up. I fumble to take them off with my mittened hand. I can't clean them—the fog is frozen on. Without my glasses, everything more than twelve inches away is a blur. But I can see better without them than with them in their frozen state. A marvelous, fuzzy world opens up to me. It seems brighter. Everything is a haze of white with dark patches of branches and a large, dark moving blob that must be my dog. Why does this memory come to mind? What is it about that cold experience that actually makes me giggle a little?

Marching from door to door in February, gathering information for the upcoming election. I can't wear my scarf over my nose—I have to be able to see out my glasses. My nose hairs are frozen. Between every house I thaw them a little by breathing into my mitten. My feet aren't cold any more. Maybe they're just numb, but I don't think so. I think the walking actually warmed them up. Three hours of this, and then I head home. The house is too warm. It hurts to go from one temperature extreme to the other. My feet were happy walking; now they burn a bit. I've never felt that before. I'm strangely proud of myself. I conquered something. Not the cold. Not winter. Something inside of me.

I feel defiant. Exhilarated. Exhausted. I have endured. I have won some bragging rights, at least among my wussy West Coast friends. Who among them has ventured into sub-zero temperatures and returned with pride and accomplishment? Admire me, please. Be in awe of my bravery. Shake your head and say, "I could never do that. I could never live there." Yes, that's it—I'm better than you now. I am *living* in Edmonton. I know what 40 below feels like. I don't like it. But I've experienced it. I've conquered it.

WINTER HEART

MICHELLE WARD-KANTOR

That blissful urge to revisit
all that has meaning

when tucked beneath the stillness
cover of dusty white

To wrestle inhibitions
places lost over time
friendships comforts passions
missed

Try to burrow beneath
your heart
in winter

Truth
laid bare
as that summer picture
when nakedness
was easy
warm enveloping a caress on your skin
as stark
as the frost-laden trees
now resting
beneath the feet of the
hawk

And you're lucky enough to catch sight
of the magnificent outreach of wings
as it leaves
its perch

Bold in the frigid air

Fading light in the early afternoon
leaves you silent
inhaling the dusky freshness, feel the clearing
in your head

footsteps crackle
bite on skin urges you
to rejoice
a child
cheeks joyful pink
running through whiteness
laughter hanging in fog breath

Realizing that is all the truth
you need

A SOLITARY SNOWFLAKE

SERENA WARD-KANTOR (AGE 12)

I am the first. I feel a mixture of pride and loneliness. I am the first! But I am alone. Being the first takes bravery. Falling through the silent space, plummeting into the unknown. There is no sound, no wind on my many arms. Only quiet. It's peaceful up here. The solitude gives me time to think about what's to come. But I don't dread melting yet. I am too consumed by curiosity.

I can see large patches of green and blue, coming up fast in front of me. Whoosh! Now there is sound, rushing in my ears and arms. The huge green patch comes closer, and I see that it is not one big patch, but millions of tiny ones. As I fall farther, there are new sounds I have never heard, new sights I have never seen. Bright lights, low hums, and hundreds of voices calling out fill my eyes and ears.

As I am blown along gently, huge eyes stare up at me, and hands reach out and try to catch me. I am welcomed warmly by excited voices calling out my name. Bright and soft colours alike dance in the sun-light. Fiery reds and oranges, soft greens and greys.

It's warmer now. The wind is soft instead of harsh and fast. I'm close to the end of my descent. I catch a glimpse of something huge and fuzzy before I land on a soft red blanket. Huge eyes stare down at me in awe, and a small voice calls out. I can feel myself getting warmer. I know the end is coming, but melting doesn't scare me as much as it did. After all, I'm happy here. Another pair of eyes catches sight of me, just before I melt into nothingness.

BARN OWL IN SNOW

ARABELLE WARD-KANTOR (AGE 9)

ICICLES AND OTHER WINTER WONDERS

ROBIN YOUNG

Everyone in Edmonton knows about icicles. They form when warm winter sunlight melts snow and ice on roofs and parked cars and anything else that has accumulated snow. Water slowly drips off the edges of roofs, the tips of tree branches, overhead wires, bridge decks, cars and, well, anywhere really that water can drip. They are winter's stalactites, but instead of taking years, they form sometimes in minutes, creating crystalline sculptures sparkling in the sunlight that created them, begging to be photographed and then broken off the overhang and passed to greedy mittened hands to be licked and sucked and savoured by youngsters who will never forget the special taste of winter contained in those icy spikes. A trace of dust, a soupcon of shingle, maybe a dash of leftover summer pollen define the taste of a well-aged (less than 24 hours) icicle. Young tongues and lips shape the ice into spikes with tips as sharp as sewing needles (mothers think of put-out eyes and pierced cheeks, but that NEVER happens), then tiny white teeth bite off the tips and crunch the ice between quickly freezing molars. When it's gone there is nothing left but some tiny grit and a taste that can only be described as "winter".

In Edmonton we have these icicles, the normal icicles of winter. True, we have them longer than many other cities in Canada, but for all of that, they are the same family as those other cities. But we have other winter wonders we produce when the mercury falls to temperatures that other, milder Canadian cities and their even more southern American cousins never experience. Here are a few examples:

Tearcicles - the long frozen strands that spread from winter cyclists' eyes as they ride along dangerously narrowed icy streets at temperatures below −25! This type of activity also produces the less appealing, but no less fantastic, "snotcicles." Ewwww.

Fogcicles - Most often seen by firefighters putting water on a blaze in the midst of winter's blast. The appropriately named "fog-nozzle" creates a wall of mist that shields nearby buildings from a raging blaze, or turns instantly to steam on contact with heat and flame, cooling, dissipating and extinguishing a fire. Not all of this beneficial mist reaches the fire. Some of it also blows back towards the wielder of the hose. Tiny particles, water droplets almost too small to see, drift onto the protective clothing of the firefighter and freeze instant-ly. Then they invite their friends over. By the time the fire is out, the firefighter looks like a surreal ice sculpture with the whole front of his gear covered in an icy shroud. If he could let go of the hose and somehow slip out of his gear, the ice simulacrum could continue to fight the fire until spring.

Fishcicles - every ice fisherman knows what these are: you catch a fish, toss it out of the hut onto the ice of the lake outside and when it is time to pack up and go home—fishcicles!

Popcicles - and not the ones you buy at Mac's. These happen when you pour your cola at −30 and make an instant slushy! You can also make **coffecicles** this way, or the more expensive **Starbuckscicles**.

Beercicles - form when you are trying to pour a beer into a glass at −35. Diehard Edmonton patio beer drinkers are familiar with these. It puts a whole new spin on "sucking down a cold one!"

Peecicles - what happens when a guy urinates en plein air at −40. This also leads to the local idiom, "Don't shake it, you'll break it!" Who does this, you ask? Who is crazy enough to try this at −40? No one I know lately, but I guarantee you, some guy you know did this. Once.

Breathcicles - When the mercury dips below −40 and you are out at the off-leash area walking the dog, breathing through your scarf which you have wisely wrapped around your face, the water vapour you exhale freezes on contact with the air. Some of it sticks to your scarf and builds up into miniature snowdrifts, crystal mounds with a steaming hole in the centre looking like a frozen volcano on your face.

If you shake your head these breathflakes fall and you are a walking weather system, snowing as you go. But where are the breathcicles? They are insidious. They form under the crust of snow on your scarf (or balaclava) and they creep slowly down among the fibres of your skin-protecting layer. They melt and merge and meld until they form a solid mass you don't even notice until you pull your scarf off later.

Winter in this northernmost capital produces some or all of these "cicles" every year. They form a part of winter's stage setting that transforms Edmonton for six (or more) months every year. Maybe we don't notice them as much as we used to when we were younger, before the cold settled so deeply in our bones. As you rush from the warm car or bus to the next shelter from winter's icy blasts, take a look around. See how many you can spot. Some of them are hard to see; others are odd or rare. But sometime this winter you should pluck a fresh icicle and touch it to your tongue. There are sights and sounds and smells of the seasons in Edmonton, but the one that brings it home is the taste of winter in the first lick of an icicle, fresh picked from the eaves of the garage. Bon appetit!

CROSS-COUNTRY SKIING TO WORK

WENDY DAVIS

I love the snow and sunshine winters in Edmonton. I emigrated from Scotland, and there we had constant rain. I never seemed to dry out. In the Highlands we had minimal snow, and skiing was mainly "heather-hopping" from one wet porridge mound of snow patch to another. One memory I have is of a friend who enjoyed smoking his pipe when skiing. He adapted to the rain by reversing his pipe.

I would save up my two weeks holiday to ski in Europe where I would be assured of snow and where the ski runs were wonderful. However, it took one week of my holiday to get my body functioning for skiing. Then the second week when finally I felt in rhythm physically and mentally with the fabulous skiing, it was time to return to the U.K. and rain. Imagine my delight when I came to Edmonton and I could cross-country ski from my front door in Belgravia. I skied regularly to work. I did not appreciate the house owners who were up before 7am shoveling their sidewalks, as when I was gliding swiftly on the snowy sidewalk there would suddenly be no snow and I would have to take off my skis. This broke my rhythm and interfered with the pleasure of the soft downy snow beneath my skis. I skied across the playing fields of McKernan School before the children were going to school. The main roads were obstacles, as I had to take off my skis at 109th Street and 82nd Avenue. However, I was never late for work.

The lamplights guided my route and were the stars of the early morning. The trees were often in an arabesque with their snow-covered branches partnering with the neighbouring trees on the other side of the road, reminding me of ballet dancers. I was not the only one up early. I left a breakfast of peanuts for the blue jays. They rewarded me with their musical calls. The magpies were visible still in their dinner jackets. Nature in an urban setting was always enjoyable when cross-country skiing to work.

One very blizzardy snowy morning, everyone in Edmonton was late for work. On my arriving at work, one of the night staff told me the CBC wanted stories of how people came to work and what hazard they had overcome. I telephoned and explained I always skied to work when there was adequate snow. Today I was on time for work, but because of the poor visibility and blowing wind, I had nearly collided with a bicycle which was also on the sidewalk. I explained that skiing to work gave me great pleasure because there was always nature to enjoy, even in urban Edmonton. The CBC was delighted that I successfully cross-country skied to work, and I would be rewarded with a special CBC mug.

Fifteen years after I retired, I reluctantly gave up skiing and took up photography. One of my favourite outings with the photo club was to the Ukrainian Village, which is a few miles east of Edmonton. In the quietness of the snow-covered countryside surrounding the village, I can close my eyes and believe I am gliding on my skis through the un-tracked sparkling snow. If I close my eyes very tightly, in my memory I can even see my friend downhill skiing on the Scottish porridge with his pipe reversed because of the rain.

Now I am 84 years old and no longer skiing to work. I still love Edmonton winters, even when the temperatures are 40 below. I rejoice in having silk underwear to keep me warm, a beautiful weeping birch gilded with snow, the chickadees performing Cirque du Soleil acrobatics on its branches. My own warm home, wonderful sunshine and good friends make Edmonton winters just fine.

THE FOX DRIVE LUGE

BEN MURRAY

No toboggan flew faster, farther
than the cardboard I rode on the hill
above Fox Drive that snowy snow day
I was Gilles Villeneuve, I was Evil Knievel
on a magic cardboard carpet skimming
December at a million miles an hour
We raced, I raced by the wipe-out sprawl
of my friends, the only one still defying
gravity, halfway down the hill now and
picking up speed, more speed, eyes blinded
by spit, raining snow, I was no longer a boy
tobogganing down a hill I was pure blur
and wind and chill and I rejoiced, my heart
leaping tall bushes in a single bound, and I shrieked
fine-line shriek bordering hilarity and terror,
the shriek of the roller-coastered, the shriek of
one who knows he's won the race even as I realized that
I can't stop! Fox Drive, the actual road and its
cars, suddenly right there, here, I was in it, I'd zoomed
right into the road as a car honked and swerved and just
missed this speed-barrier boy with cardboard wings
and I stopped (insert cartoon screech here)
I finally stopped, still breathing, I was
alive, and I saw the driver across the road, standing
by his vehicle, still a human question mark, still a shocked
man not quite believing his eyes, so before he did
I ran
I turned around and fled, back up the hill, hollering to
my friends "Run!" "Run!"— and we raced up that Fox
Driven mountain hill not looking back once
till our lungs verged on bursting, till we were blocks

away from that car, that swerving, probably swearing
man
and later we sat in our snug Belgravian homes, shaking,
dreading the next knock on the door, the swerving man
standing there, all rage and glare and wrath—he never did come
but some thirty Edmonton winters later
I still sometimes remember that wild ride and wonder
who's that knocking at my door?